Managing Infrastructure Projects

World Scientific Series on the Built Environment

Series Editor: Willie Chee Keong Tan
(National University of Singapore, Singapore)

World Scientific Series on the Built Environment

Volume 3

Managing Infrastructure Projects

Willie Tan

National University of Singapore, Singapore

World Scientific

NEW JERSEY · LONDON · SINGAPORE · BEIJING · SHANGHAI · HONG KONG · TAIPEI · CHENNAI · TOKYO

Published by

World Scientific Publishing Co. Pte. Ltd.
5 Toh Tuck Link, Singapore 596224
USA office: 27 Warren Street, Suite 401-402, Hackensack, NJ 07601
UK office: 57 Shelton Street, Covent Garden, London WC2H 9HE

Library of Congress Control Number: 2021936891

British Library Cataloguing-in-Publication Data
A catalogue record for this book is available from the British Library.

World Scientific Series on the Built Environment — Vol. 3
MANAGING INFRASTRUCTURE PROJECTS

ISBN 978-981-123-958-8 (hardcover)
ISBN 978-981-123-959-5 (paperback)
ISBN 978-981-123-963-2 (ebook for institutions)
ISBN 978-981-123-964-9 (ebook for individuals)

For any available supplementary material, please visit
https://www.worldscientific.com/worldscibooks/10.1142/12350#t=suppl

Desk Editor: Amanda Yun

Typeset by Stallion Press
Email: enquiries@stallionpress.com

Preface

This book is about practical ways to manage the infrastructure development cycle from project initiation to the end of the operation and maintenance phase. It focuses on the Public-Private Partnership (PPP) contract and, from this perspective, private and public sector procurement are variations. Project management is about managing time, cost, quality, safety, and risks using project management methodologies, risk instruments, as well as regulatory, governance, and contract structures. If we leave these critical activities to intuition, projects are likely to fail.

The idea of writing this book originates from a series of Development Finance lectures in the MSc (Project Management) program at the Department of Building, School of Design and Environment, National University of Singapore. The students come from diverse backgrounds such as information technology, business, architecture, quantity surveying, urban planning, project management, engineering, construction, facilities management, transport, finance, economics, and law. The book provides a structured guide to these diverse students as well as to researchers, public officials, project sponsors, lenders, developers, contractors, subcontractors, suppliers, investors, infrastructure fund managers, insurers, facilities managers, non-government organizations, and consultants such as designers, engineers, environmental specialists, legal advisors, and brokers.

My approach is to focus on general principles that are practical and applicable in different countries, particularly in the developing world where markets, regulatory, and other institutions are less developed. Hence, the book uses many examples to illustrate applications and avoids detailed case studies. The book deals with only the main processes, leaving it to the reader to explore the details from standard textbooks in project finance and project management.

The infrastructure development cycle is considerably longer than the usual project cycle found in standard textbooks on project management. There are many stakeholders in an infrastructure project. Hence, we may view the management of such projects from different perspectives. This book focuses on the role of the public *grantor* during the initial phases of identification, feasibility study, project preparation, risk allocation, and public tender. It then considers the private *sponsor's* bid preparation, the *lender's* due diligence, and the PPP contract award. Thereafter, we track the sponsor's pre-construction activities to establish the special purpose vehicle, set up the project governance structure, design the project, and prepare for construction tender. If it is a Design-Build or Engineering, Procurement, and Construction (EPC) project delivery method, then the *contractor* is also responsible for the design. During the mobilization and project execution phases, the discussion shifts to the relation between the sponsor and contractor. Upon project completion, the sponsor appoints an *operator* to manage the operation and maintenance. Finally, towards the end of the PPP contract, we consider the handing over arrangements from the sponsor to the grantor.

Project terminology differs across countries, sectors, and analysts. In this book, the grantor is the ceding authority, public agency, or public entity. The sponsor is the client, owner, developer, or employer depending on the context. Sometimes, we use the plural form, that is, sponsors instead of sponsor. "Designers" are architects, engineers, and other design professionals. The following terms are similar: bid or tender, variation order or change order, and contract or agreement. This differs from the use of an "agreement" as an unenforceable private understanding or arrangement. I use the pronoun "he" or "she" interchangeably, and "log x" instead of "ln x" for natural logarithm to avoid confusing "n" with sample size.

I assume readers are familiar with basic project management, economics, finance, calculus, and statistics or data analytics. Where possible, I avoid the heavy mathematics and focus on intuitive understanding of the problems and solutions. I also use many examples to put theories into perspectives.

I thank the following academics and practitioners for their helpful suggestions on the structure of the book and chapters: Alexander Lin, Bijay Joseph, Imriyas Kamardeen, Calvin Yeung, Christopher Leong,

Dilini Thoradeniya, Eoon Hoon Eng, Eugene Seah, Jeffrey Tan, Jonathan Lian, Josh Ng, Li Dezhi, Lim Pin, Neo Kim Han, Ravi Shankar, Shen Liyin, Stephen Tay, Winston Hauw, and Zhang Yajian.

Lastly, I thank Amanda Yun, Senior Editor, World Scientific, for her kind assistance and encouragement to bring this book to fruition amid my busy schedule and disruptions due to the COVID-19 pandemic.

Willie Tan

Note on currency use in the book: Unless otherwise stated, all references/use of the $ symbol refers to Singapore Dollars (SGD).

List of abbreviations

AEI —   asset enhancement initiatives

BIM —   Building Information Modeling
BOT —   Build-Operate-Transfer
BOO —   Build-Operate-Own
BTO —   Build-Transfer-Operate
BVI —   British Virgin Islands

CBA —   cost-benefit analysis
CDW —   construction and demolition waste
CEA —   cost-effectiveness analysis
CIF —   cost, insurance and freight
CM —   Construction Management/Manager
CMA —   cost-minimization analysis
CMMS —   computerized maintenance management software
CONQUAS —   Construction Quality Assessment System
CSC —   certificate of statutory completion
CV —   cost variance

DB —   Design-Build
DBB —   Design-Bid-Build
DBFO —   Design-Build-Finance-Operate
DBO —   Design-Build-Operate
DBOO —   Design-Build-Operate-Own
DLP —   defects liability period
DWBS —   design work breakdown structure

EPC —   Engineering, Procurement, and Construction
ECI —   Early Contractor Involvement

EF —	early finish
ES —	early start
FC —	foreign currency
FM —	Force majeure
FOB —	free on board
GL —	general liability
GMP —	Guaranteed Maximum Price
HVAC —	heating, ventilation and air conditioning
IMF —	International Monetary Fund
IPD —	Integrated Project Delivery
IRR —	internal rate of return
JV —	joint venture
LC —	local currency
LEED —	Leadership in Energy and Environmental Design
LF —	late finish
LLC —	limited liability company
LLP —	limited liability partnership
LS —	late start
MCS —	Monte Carlo simulation
MOE —	Ministry of Environment
NGO —	non-government organization
NLA —	net lettable area
NPV —	net present value
NTP —	Notice to Proceed
O&M —	Operation and Maintenance
OER —	official exchange rate
OMETA —	operation, maintenance, engineering support, training, and administration

PDCA — Plan-Do-Check-Act
PDE — partial differential equation
PM —
PPP — Public Private Partnership

QA — quality assurance
QC — quality control

R&D — research and development
RFP — Request for Proposal
RFQ — Request for Qualification
RMB — Renminbi

SIBOR — Singapore Interbank Offered Rate
SBM — Standard Brownian Movement
SER — shadow exchange rate
SGA — selling, general, and administrative expenses
SOP — standard operating procedure
SORA — Singapore Overnight Rate Average
SPE — special purpose entity
SPV — special purpose vehicle, project entity, or project company

TOP — temporary occupation permit
TQM — total quality management

VfM — value for money
VO — variation order

WBS — work breakdown structure
WTA — willing(ness) to accept
WTE — waste-to-energy
WTP — willing(ness) to pay

Contents

CHAPTER 1

Introduction to infrastructure

Physical infrastructure

Infrastructure refers to durable physical systems that support economic and social activities of a city or country. The physical infrastructure consists of economic and social infrastructure. The former includes

- utilities (water, electricity, and gas);
- transport networks (road, rail, sea, and air);
- waste management systems; and
- communication and information technology systems.

The social infrastructure consists of facilities such as

- schools and institutions of higher learning;
- prisons and hospitals;
- sports and recreational facilities; and
- religious buildings.

A more general definition of infrastructure includes residential units, factories, offices, and commercial buildings.

Soft infrastructure

An even broader definition of infra structure includes the "soft" side, that is, the institutions of society that govern common undertakings within the community. Examples of soft infrastructure include

- public and private organizations;
- laws, regulations, and rules;

- social norms; and
- social or business networks.

Organizations such as firms, clubs, religious bodies, government ministries, hospitals, and schools are institutions because they have their own rules. They are the institutional players (North, 1990).

The laws, regulations, and rules of a society cover property rights, currencies, weight and measures, land use zoning, health and safety, and so on. These rules govern the behavior of individuals.

Social norms are unwritten rules of acceptable social behavior, such as the expectation of punctuality and being courteous. Not all norms increase social welfare; some norms may be discriminatory, such as those relating to marriage, gender, and race. These norms may restrict the choices or wishes of those affected, such as the decision to get married, have children, and so on.

There are also rules that govern behavior in social and business networks. Some of these rules are unwritten; that is, they are norms, especially in social networks. Business networks may have explicit rules. These networks tend to benefit members by sharing ideas, resources, and opportunities (Orru *et al.*, 1996). However, they can also have negative effects. For example, close kinship ties can impose certain unwanted obligations on members (Hyden, 2012) or cut off suppliers that are more competitive.

Despite these downsides, norms and networks are sometimes considered as the "social capital" of society (Banfield, 1958; Putnam, 2001), unlike natural, physical, human, or financial capital. They function like "capital" because of their ability to increase production by reducing the transaction costs of doing business or solving collection action problems (Ostrom, 1990), such as by developing trust (Fukuyama, 1995; Ghate *et al.*, 2008), sharing of business information, monitoring performance, mediating disputes, and punishing cheaters (Coase, 1937).

Ownership and performance

Ownership of physical infrastructure may be private, public, or mixed, such as the mix of public and private power generation plants, roads, schools, universities, hospitals, and sports facilities.

It is sometimes argued that public managers face weaker incentives because they rely on public funding, do not face threats of takeover if performance falters, pursue political and social objectives, and are difficult to monitor for performance (Frydman *et al.*, 1999).

However, it is not clear that private managers act in the interests of shareholders if they own little stock, that is, there is the well-known problem of corporate separation between ownership and control. Further, according to neoclassical economic theory, if the private firm is operating as a monopoly, there will be productive inefficiencies and welfare loss through higher prices.

Based on the above arguments, we see that ownership of infrastructure assets may matter less for performance than the business environment of its operation and capital market discipline by lenders and investors (Vickers and Yarrow, 1991). It is by no means clear that the public sector is less efficient.

Infrastructure investment

Most countries invest around two to eight percent of their annual Gross Domestic Product (GDP) on infrastructure, and the world average is around four percent. Based on the global nominal output of goods and services of US$88 trillion in 2019, this works out to about US$3.5 trillion a year, or US$35 trillion over the next decade.

Currently, because of poor economic performance, large fiscal debt, war, and other reasons, many countries underinvest in infrastructure. The resulting shortfall is about US$350 billion a year over the next decade (McKinsey Global Institute, 2016). This is unfortunate because infrastructure investment confers many benefits such as

- lower transport and communication costs;
- greater production because of better access to markets and inter-firm linkages;
- reduction of spoilage of inputs, intermediate goods, and outputs;
- sharing of ideas through information technology and communications infrastructure;

- greater access to financing by helping to develop domestic capital markets;
- income and employment generation;
- improving access to facilities, education, healthcare, and job opportunities for the poor;
- reduction in regional inequalities;
- short-run stabilization of the economy through Keynesian demand management during recessions and, conversely, the reduction in public infrastructure spending during economic booms to curb inflation;
- more sustainable development by reducing traffic congestion, pollution, and promoting the use of renewable energy; and
- more resilient development by mitigating the adverse effects of climate change and viral attacks.

Some considerations are political, such as regional development, access for the poor, income and employment generation, and economic stabilization. Hence, it is possible to over-invest in infrastructure, such as building airports, bridges, and hospitals in declining regions that do not require them.

Infrastructure as an asset class

Infrastructure is an asset class because it generates stable long-term cash flows, which makes it attractive to public and institutional investors looking for opportunities to diversify their investment portfolios. For example, insurers will be able to match their long-term assets and liabilities by investing in infrastructure. The investment returns are largely unrelated to fluctuations in the short-term business cycle because of the long-lived nature of infrastructure assets. For example, the dividend yield of Keppel Investment Trust (KIT) has been relatively stable despite the COVID-19 pandemic (Table 1.1).

There are many ways to invest in infrastructure assets. It may be direct through project equity participation or indirect through infrastructure funds, real estate investment trusts (REITs), and securitized infrastructure loans. To securitize a loan or asset is to convert its value as sellable

Table 1.1 Dividend yield of KIT.

Year	Dividend yield (%)
2020	5.21
2019	6.95
2018	6.95
2017	6.95
2016	5.21

securities that are then sold to investors. For the owners of these loans or assets, securitization frees up tied-up capital. Unlike home mortgages where securitization comes with higher risks of default because of changes in mortgage interest rates (Shiller, 2008), infrastructure assets, when pooled, tend to provide more stable returns.

Long waves of infrastructure investment

Some analysts claimed the existence of "long waves" of infrastructure investment that are less regular than post-World War II short-term business cycles and with a period of about 40 to 60 years (Van Duijin, 1983).

These waves have many possible causes such as

- the replacement of long-lived infrastructure (Kondratiev, 1935);
- clustering of technological innovation (Schumpeter, 1939);
- institutional changes in the structures of capital accumulation (Aglietta, 1979; Bowles *et al.*, 1983);
- long-term variations in the profit rate (Mandel, 1999);
- demographics (see Tylecote, 1991); and
- war (Goldstein, 1988).

There is no consensus on the theory and evidence on long waves. It is difficult to build a theory to explain long-term capitalist development in a country or on a global scale. The empirical evidence is also scant because of the need to observe long periods of upswings and downswings (Berry, 1991).

Sustainable infrastructure

Infrastructure projects should be ecologically sustainable. This requires adherence to four principles of sustainability, namely,

- the precautionary principle to safeguard the environment, particularly irreversible damage, if there are insufficient scientific evidence on the ecological impacts of projects;
- inter-generational equity so that future generations do not inherit a worse-off environment;
- conservation of biological diversity and ecological integrity so that different species can survive; and
- inclusion of environmental factors in valuing assets, such as the use of cost-benefit analysis (CBA) in evaluating projects.

Governments may mitigate carbon emissions by using a mixture of regulation, taxes, and trading.

Carbon regulation involves the "command and control" fixing, measuring, monitoring, and enforcing emission standards. This regulatory oversight using physical controls is complex, and requires considerable effort and trial and error. Further, firms have no incentive to cut back on allowable levels of pollution. Hence, economists prefer carbon taxes or carbon trading although these measures have downsides as well.

A carbon tax will encourage major carbon producers to reduce their carbon emissions. Such taxes are often politically difficult to impose. Consequently, in most countries, the tax rate is modest and insufficient to spur substantial reductions in emissions. Producers may also threaten to pass the higher cost to "angry" consumers. For example, the Australian government imposed a carbon tax of A$23 per ton in 2012 but reversed it the next year. Nonetheless, many governments have imposed the carbon tax. They use the tax revenue to fund projects to mitigate climate change or distribute it to consumers as carbon dividends to compensate for the higher energy costs.

In carbon trading, the government sets the annual cap on carbon emissions and allocates or sells these allowances. Firms that can cut back substantially on their emissions will have excess allowances, and they can sell them to firms that require these allowances. The annual cap is flexible, and carbon markets may be regional, national, or international. Like carbon taxes, "cap and trade" systems have their share of political difficulties. The main concern is the reluctance of many governments to impose costs on industry and consumers, resulting in weak caps. In turn, the large supply of allowances leads to low carbon prices. For example, in the European Union (EU) market, prices fell from €30 to €4 per ton between 2008 and 2013. Since then, the impact of climate change has forced a rethink on carbon trading. With stronger caps, EU carbon prices have climbed back steadily to around €25 in early 2021.

The United Nations (UN) project-based Clean Development Mechanism (CDM) started in 2005 and works slightly differently from the "cap and trade" system. It allows governments and firms in rich countries to buy certified carbon credits (CCCs) from poor countries. This arrangement benefits the poor countries by encouraging the development of green projects to earn CCCs. The project originator sells these credits through a broker to finance part of the project. However, like the "cap and trade" system, participation in CDM fluctuates with carbon prices.

At the global level, efforts to reduce carbon emissions such as the Paris Agreement (2015) tend to suffer from collective action problems. A country that does not agree with the terms of the agreement is unlikely to contribute towards the Green Climate Fund to reduce greenhouse gas emissions.

Resilient infrastructure

A resilient infrastructure system is able to function during and after a disaster or adapt to climate change. Such a system will avoid expensive repairs after a hazard, reduce disruptions to economic and social activities, improve human well-being, and minimize human injuries and fatalities.

There are two ways to promote the development of resilient systems. The management approach (Gardoni, 2020) includes

- modeling the impact of climate change and hazards on infrastructure;
- better maintenance and repairs;

- developing effective emergence responses;
- developing a disaster mitigation plan; and
- modeling the recovery of physical and socio-economic systems.

The design or planning approach (Infield *et al.*, 2019) focuses on

- altering urban form, such as to reduce transport costs or the urban heat island effect;
- technical design of physical systems;
- proper siting of infrastructure systems;
- use of protective landscaping;
- building resilience in project procurement; and
- promotion of more self-sufficient regions to mitigate serious supply disruptions.

Both approaches require effective institutions to support the design, management, and implementation of resilient measures. Since the impact will be uneven across different regions and social groups, an inclusive and just strategy is also required to build resilient infrastructure (Sarte and Stipisic, 2016).

Infrastructure challenges

Providing infrastructure is often a challenge for governments. The common problems often relate to

- political authority and autonomy;
- strategies and objectives;
- project governance;
- assessment of social, economic, and environmental performance;
- funding;
- land acquisition;
- project selection;
- inequitable risk allocation;
- planning and coordination;
- delivery; and
- operation and maintenance.

To be able to deliver infrastructure at different levels, governments must have the authority to act. In some countries, power is centralized and the authority of lower levels of government are limited by the constitution. In such unitary systems, the latter will need to rely on central government grants and local resources. These grants may not be predictable, making it difficult to plan and execute infrastructure projects. In terms of autonomy, politicians need to deal with the bureaucracy, social groups, and the web of complex processes, rules, and regulations. The bureaucracy may want to protect and expand turf rather than be a "servant" to its political masters.

There needs to be a long-term national vision for infrastructure development. With the COVID-19 pandemic and the resulting higher unemployment, there is now an opportunity to move strategically towards green and resilient infrastructure to create new types of industries and jobs, rather than business as usual.

The project governance structure will have to be decisive, inclusive, participatory, and involve the private sector. There has to be "buy in" from social groups that have been badly affected by the COVID-19 pandemic or groups that resist higher taxes. The poor should have access to good infrastructure, and should benefit from the creation of new jobs and industries.

We need to assess the collective responsibilities and performance of the key stakeholders with regard to the social, economic, and environmental impacts of the project. We should institutionalize the assessment as part of project design, rather than as ad hoc reactive or passive responses.

Funding will always be an issue given current fiscal deficits, especially after the COVID-19 pandemic. Many governments will continue to incur high debts as the pandemic drags. Yet, amid this fiscal drag, the land acquisition process needs to be fair and efficient to avoid contentious challenges and long delays.

Project selection should be based on priorities and standards to ascertain infrastructure deficits. There needs to be proper evaluation of benefits and costs based on evidence, and there should not be a bias for new-build over rehabilitation projects. The government has to allocate the risks efficiently and equitably and not saddle the private sector with excessive risks.

Governments also need to strengthen their capacity to plan and coordinate projects through staff training and adequate provision of resources. Similarly, public agencies need to integrate their infrastructure investment plans into the national and city master plans and coordinate the implementation.

There are different delivery models such as

- direct provision by central government units;
- provision by lower government levels or agencies;
- private provision; and
- public-private partnerships (PPP).

These choices affect the project funding, coordination, risks, design, construction, and operation.

Finally, the operation and maintenance of infrastructure may be direct, delegated, privately executed, or carried out under a PPP arrangement. The traditional division of labor between central line ministries and lower levels of governments can cause problems if the latter are poorly funded and not consulted for design or construction inputs.

References

Aglietta, M. (1979) *A theory of capitalist regulation*. London: Verso.

Banfield, E. (1958) *The moral basis of a backward society*. New York: Free Press.

Berry, B. (1991) *Long-wave rhythms in economic development and political behavior*. Baltimore: Johns Hopkins University Press.

Bowles, S., Gordon, D., and Weisskopf, T. (1983) *Beyond the wasteland*. New York: Anchor Books.

Coase, R. (1937) The nature of the firm. *Economica*, 4(16), 386–405.

Frydman, R., Gray, C., Hessel, M., and Rapaczynski, A. (1999) When does privatization work? *Quarterly Journal of Economics*, 114(4), 1153–1191.

Fukuyama, F. (1995) *Trust*. New York: Free Press.

Gardoni, P. (Ed.) (2020) *Routledge handbook of sustainable and resilient infrastructure*. London: Routledge.

Ghate, R. Jodha, N., and Mukhopadhyay, P. (2008) *Promise, trust, and evolution: Managing the commons of South Asia*. New York: Oxford University Press.

Goldstein, J. (1988) *Long cycles: Prosperity and war in the modern Age*. New Haven: Yale University Press.

Hyden, G. (2012) *The economy of affection*. London: Cambridge University Press.

Infield, E., Abunnasr, Y., and Ryan, R. (Eds.) (2019) *Planning for climate change*. London: Taylor and Francis.

Kondratiev, N. (1935) The long waves in economic life. *Review of Economic Statistics*, 17(6), 105–115.

Mandel, E. (1999) *Late capitalism*. London: Verso.

McKinsey Global Institute (2016) *Bridging global infrastructure gaps*. San Francisco: MGI.

North, D. (1990) *Institutions, institutional change and economic performance*. Cambridge: Cambridge University Press.

Orru, M., Biggart, N., and Hamilton, G. (1996) *The economic organization of East Asian capitalism*. New York: SAGE.

Ostrom, E. (1990) *Governing the commons*. New York: Cambridge University Press.

Putnam, R. (2001) *Bowling alone*. New York: Simon and Schuster.

Sarte, S. and Stipisic, M. (2016) *Water infrastructure: Equitable deployment of resilient systems*. New York: Columbia University Office of Publications.

Schumpeter, J. (1939) *Business cycles*. New York: McGraw-Hill.

Shiller, R. (2008) *The subprime solution*. New Jersey: Princeton University Press.

Tylecote, A. (1991) *The long wave in the world economy*. London: Routledge.

Van Dujin, J. (1983) *The long wave in economic life*. London: George Allen & Unwin.

Vickers, J. and Yarrow, G. (1991) Economic perspectives on privatization. *Journal of Economic Perspectives*, 5(2), 111–132.

CHAPTER 2

The stages of infrastructure development

Institutional framework

Projects are embedded within often taken-for-granted institutional frameworks so that they can be properly managed.

The elements of this institutional framework include government, political systems, organizations, markets, regulatory systems, financial systems, property rights, the legal system, and the social system (World Bank, 2002). History plays an important role in the development of institutions; for example, ex-colonies inherit different sets of institutions that set them on different growth trajectories (Acemoglu and Robinson, 2012). Countries with weak institutions need to build effective ones to support projects and generate economic growth.

The project cycle

Before discussing the infrastructure development cycle, it is useful to consider the construction project cycle, which consists of the following phases (Bennett, 2003):

- pre-project;
- planning and design;
- contractor selection;
- mobilization;
- site execution; and
- project close-out.

A slight variation is the following (Baum, 1982):

- project initiation;
- planning;
- execution;
- close-out; and
- operation and maintenance.

The main difference is that operation and maintenance is considered an additional phase after project close-out.

For other sectors, the project cycle is similar. For example, the software development cycle consists of (Philips, 2010)

- requirements gathering and analysis;
- planning and design;
- development;
- testing; and
- operation and maintenance.

There are variations, such as having a deployment phase after software testing or by combining both activities in a single phase.

Phases in infrastructure development

The infrastructure development cycle is much longer than the standard project cycle. For a Public Private Partnership (PPP) project, it consists of the following phases:

- project identification;
- appraisal of options;
- feasibility study;
- project preparation;
- tender;
- sponsor's bid preparation;
- bid evaluation and contract award;
- lender's due diligence;
- sponsor's pre-construction activities;

- mobilization;
- construction or execution;
- project close-out;
- operation and maintenance; and
- handing over.

We will discuss each phase in greater detail in subsequent chapters. Each phase consists of many sub-stages.

Like the standard project cycle, there are many variations of the infrastructure development cycle and projects may not have all the above phases. Some projects terminate at the end of the construction phase. For example, private developers may build housing units for sale and are not involved in the operation and maintenance phase. Similarly, internal projects within an organization may not involve bidding, financing, and transfer of assets at the end of the operation and maintenance period.

It is possible to terminate a project before the end of the PPP contract period. It can occur because of policy changes, default of contracting parties, prolonged force majeure events, achievement of target profit margin, unlocking of asset value, securitization of asset, and so on.

References

Acemoglu, D. and Robinson, J. (2012) *Why nations fail*. New York: Currency.

Baum, W. (1982) *The project cycle*. Washington DC: World Bank.

Bennett, L. (2003) *The management of construction*. London: Butterworth.

Philips, J. (2010) *IT project management*. New York: McGraw-Hill.

World Bank (2002) *Building institutions for markets*. Washington DC: World Bank.

CHAPTER 3

Project identification

Sources of projects

Projects arise from perceived problems, needs, or opportunities. They come largely from government infrastructure investment plans derived from economic, land use, and other strategies. There are also international projects such as those developed under China's Belt and Road Initiative (BRI) to create a huge international market for goods, services, talent, ideas, and capital. Announced in 2013, it involves infrastructure investments in Asia, Middle East, Europe, Africa, and the Americas over many decades. The "Belt" refers to overland road and rail transport, and the "Road" refers to the maritime sea routes.

Some governments are open to unsolicited proposals from the private sector. These proposals may just be initial or innovative ideas and require careful screening to avoid perceptions of corruption or its sensitive or confidential nature. If a proposal is promising, there is the issue of whether to use direct negotiation such as on cost plus fee basis or competitive tender (World Bank, 2019). In the latter, the proposer may be automatically shortlisted as a bidder, given bonus points in tender evaluation, or given the option to match the winning bid and be awarded the PPP contract. Like all proposals, there is also the issue of fiscal support throughout the duration of the PPP contract.

Infrastructure projects can stand alone or form part of a series of related projects called a *development program*. For example, a rural integrated development program may consist of the building of institutions, roads, schools, medical facilities, markets, irrigation systems, and so on (Hebbar, 1991). Similarly, a long-term housing development program may consist of the building of a series of new towns and housing estates. Unsolicited proposals may not integrate well in such programs.

Preliminary screening

Regardless of the sources of potential projects, an initial project team in the primary ministry ranks and screens them to eliminate undesirable ones. Some proposals are simply wild ideas that are unlikely to be taken seriously to save valuable time and cost.

Assessment of options

For projects that show promise, the next step is to consider possible options for each proposal.

One option is to do nothing, but only after evaluating other options by considering the demand and supply of infrastructure. On the demand side, it may be possible to reduce the demand for the infrastructure such as through appropriate pricing, or to meet it with the existing infrastructure. On the supply side, there is the option to upgrade the facility or build a new one.

For bold new ideas, particularly those in transport, there is the option of piloting some of these projects to test and learn from the experience.

Preliminary study

Given the goals and objectives, the preliminary study appraises the various options for each potential project. For example, for a new facility, it consists of

- technical assessment;
- economic appraisal; and
- political, regulatory, and legal assessment.

We discuss these items below.

Technical assessment

The technical assessment covers

- project scope and basic specifications;
- site options;

- basic design and engineering options;
- preliminary schedule;
- project governance structure;
- choice of delivery; and
- procurement strategy.

This definition of technical assessment is broad. A narrower definition restricts it to design and engineering evaluation. The project scope and basic specifications may be developed top-down or bottom-up by soliciting inputs from other stakeholders. The specification includes target users, functions, main materials, culture and aesthetics, environmental sustainability, resilience, and performance.

The study team then evaluates the site, design, and engineering options. If a site is not yet available, it will have to look for suitable sites. At this early stage, little is known about the project and the preliminary schedule is just a simple bar chart with broad timings and possible milestones.

The *project governance* structure spells out who has authority in the project, that is, the levels of decision-making, and reporting of progress. It is a high-level decision-making body comprising senior management and key stakeholders. At this stage, the structure may not be complete.

The choice of *project delivery* includes public provision, private provision, or a mixture such as PPP. If the government provides the output, it may do it centrally or delegate it to lower levels of government.

The *procurement strategy* consists of three parts, namely,

- ways of selecting contractors;
- construction delivery methods; and
- payment methods.

Contractors may be selected through open, selective, or limited tender. For infrastructure projects, open tenders are impractical considering the high cost of project preparation and complexity of the project. Hence, the most common strategy is to use a selective tender by pre-qualifying about six potential bidders. In a limited tender, there are only one or two bidders, such as in sensitive military projects.

There are many construction delivery and payment methods (Table 3.1). In the Design-Bid-Build (DBB) route, the owner engages

Table 3.1   Project delivery methods.

Project delivery	Features	Payment method
Design-Bid-Build	• Separate design and construction contracts • Award is based on lowest bid or points system	• Lump sum (fixed price) • Bills of Quantities, with possible re-measurement • Unit price
Design-Build or Engineering, Procurement, and Construction (EPC)	• Single design and construction contract • Owner may contract with design consultants first and then novate design contract to contractor • Award is based on price and technical proposals • No independent check on contractor	• Lump sum
Early Contractor Involvement (ECI)	• Owner uses contractor's input to revise design and draft tender documents before bidding • Award is based on lowest bid or points system	• Lump sum
Construction Management (CM)	• Owner engages a Construction Manager (CM) to manage the project • Owner contracts with design consultants and different trade subcontractors • Award is based on lowest bid or points system	• CM fee plus subcontractor bids subject to Guaranteed Maximum Price (GMP)
Integrated Project Delivery (IPD)	• Owner, contractor, and designers sign a multi-party contract to design and build to target cost	• Depends on performance
PPP	• Grantor and SPV sign PPP contract	• User or government pays

consultants to design the project, produce tender documents, and manage the tender process. The contract award is based on price or a points system. During construction, the consultants provide independent project control over the contractor on behalf of the owner. The payment is usually a lump sum (fixed price) and, occasionally, Bills of Quantities. For projects where quantities are uncertain (e.g. earthworks), payment is based on unit price. The DBB route provides owners with cost certainty (subject to variation orders) and independent designer control over the project. However, it is prone to disputes between designers and contractors.

A Design-Build (DB) or Engineering, Procurement, and Construction (EPC) contract provides a single point of responsibility but designers no longer exercise independent project control on behalf of the owner. The owner may engage the designers to control the conceptual design before *novating* the design contract to the contractor. The contractor then leads the design development process.

In Early Contractor Involvement (ECI), the contractor is brought in early to provide input to facilitate the integration of design and construction. ECI may be used for DBB and EPC contracts. The owner bears two additional costs, namely, the fee for the early contractor, and longer time for project design and planning before tender. The benefits are possible cost reductions based on the early contractor's inputs.

In Construction Management (CM), the owner engages designers to design the project and a construction manager to plan and manage it. The owner takes the risks of project delays and cost over-runs. A variation of this project delivery method is CM at-risk where these risks are transferred to the construction manager.

The Integrated Project Delivery (IPD) approach is governed by a collaborative multi-party contract to design and build to target cost. There is no bidding; the owner negotiates and selects the team based on perceptions of quality and past dealings. The parties share the risks, and payment depends on performance rather than price competition. However, whether the parties will collaborate is an empirical question, and IPD may not attract financing. Lenders prefer fixed price contracts and tested clauses.

In a Public Private Partnership (PPP) project (Fig. 3.1), the government entity or agency (also called the grantor, ceding authority, or contracting authority) enters into a PPP contract with the special purpose vehicle (SPV, project entity, or project company). The SPV designs, builds, finances, operates, and maintains the infrastructure to specifications and earns revenues from it during the contract or concession period (e.g. 25 years). The SPV may upgrade an existing asset rather than build a new one.

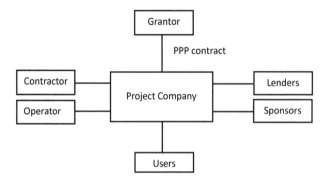

Fig. 3.1   PPP contract structure.

Sponsors are active equity owners of the project company and conduct their businesses through a shareholders' agreement. They raise and contribute the initial equity and borrow the rest through a loan agreement. Lending is on limited recourse, that is, lenders have recourse to only project cash flows and assets if the project fails. There is often limited support from sponsors or their parent companies, such as contingent equity and guarantees. Lenders require sponsors to establish the SPV to "ring fence" the project assets and cash flows as security for the loan.

The SPV then engages a contractor through a construction contract to build the facility and, upon completion, appoints an operator using an operation and maintenance contract. It then sells the output through an off-take contract or directly to users. The other stakeholders include regulators, subcontractors, suppliers, insurers, rating agencies, and consultants. There are many external stakeholders such as foreign governments, the mass media, affected residents and businesses, non-government organizations (NGOs), environmentalists, and development aid agencies.

At the end of the contract period, the SPV may own the asset or transfer it to the government. The former is a Design-Build-Operate-Own (DBOO) arrangement, and the latter is a Build-Operate-Transfer (BOT) model. Both models are also called Design-Build-Finance-Operate (DBFO) arrangements with or without transfer of asset. Generally, whether there is transfer of assets depends on the residual value and whether the land is privately or publicly owned.

The two main PPP payment models are

- grantor pays; and
- user pays.

The "grantor pays" model has three variations, namely,

- availability basis;
- output basis; or
- input basis.

In general, the grantor pays for the "availability" of the facility in cases where there is little or no private demand, such as schools, prisons, sports facilities, and public hospitals. For example, the grantor pays for the use of the prison irrespective of the number of prisoners. The grantor may also be an off-taker that purchases the project output, such as electricity or desalinated water. Finally, the grantor may pay for the input, such as municipal solid waste in waste-to-energy (WTE) incinerator projects.

Users pay for the project output or service if there is private demand, such as toll roads, bridges, and railways.

Governments have several reasons for using the PPP route. They may want to tap on private funds to overcome fiscal constraints in building infrastructure and achieve earlier project completion. PPP projects also provide better *value for money* (VfM) through

- competition and transparency in project bids;
- cost efficiency;
- private sector expertise and innovation;
- capacity building and opportunity to learn from the private sector;
- rigorous assessment of project feasibility;
- opportunities for risk sharing and transfer;
- whole life consideration of design, construction, operation, and maintenance;
- accountability and service performance by linking payment to performance;
- opportunities to share the use of facilities with other users to lower the total cost to the public;

- opportunities to generate and share third-party revenue; and
- possible transfer of asset to the grantor at the end of the concession period.

Some governments use PPP as an opportunity or catalyst for structural reforms such as privatization, deregulation, and development of the local financial sector in infrastructure lending, insurance, and financial management of risks. Global lenders such as the World Bank and International Monetary Fund (IMF) may require a government to implement structural reforms as a condition for loans.

The possible downsides to the use of PPP include

- higher financing cost of about two to three percent, assuming the government can borrow at a lower cost of capital;
- higher transaction cost of searching for information, negotiation, monitoring, and settling of disputes because of contractual complexity;
- possible user affordability issues if the SPV subsequently raises the price of output;
- safety, environmental, and service quality concerns because of the profit motive; and
- possible lack of participation by private sector if the risks are perceived to be too high or improperly allocated.

The issue of whether the profit motive results in safety, environmental, and service quality concerns is debatable.

Economic appraisal

The second component of a preliminary study is economic appraisal, also known as *cost-benefit analysis* (CBA). It is used to study the efficiency effects of policy changes, such as the impact of a liquor tax on buyers and sellers or the impact of a rent subsidy program on house prices. These analyses may be found in microeconomics textbooks for public policy analyses (e.g. Levy, 1995).

A second use of CBA, which concerns us here, is the appraisal of public projects from a resource point of view. CBA uses the competitive market and monetary value to compare different projects to improve resource allocation. It differs from private sector financial analyses that focus on profitability.

A final use of CBA is social impact analysis of government intervention, particularly who gains and who loses (Derman and Whiteford, 2019). It provides a more targeted approach to assess the impact on different groups.

A related tool for economic analysis is *cost-minimization analysis* (CMA). Here, we compare two projects or programs with identical output and search for the least-cost solution. If the outputs differ only in a single dimension, we can use *cost-effectiveness analysis* (CEA). It measures benefit in physical units, such as quantity of water treated per dollar spent. In this case, we are comparing two water treatment plants that differ only in capacity. CEA is less useful if a project generates many benefits because it is difficult to aggregate physical units without using monetary values. Hence, CBA is broader than CMA and CEA because the analyst considers many types of benefits and costs (Drummond *et al.*, 1997).

Economic appraisal using CBA focuses on social welfare and not private profitability. For market demand to reflect the social benefit of consuming a good, we need to assume that the existing distribution of income is acceptable. In Fig. 3.2, the economic benefit of a project with output Q^* in a competitive market is the area $A + B + C$. It is the area under demand curve (D) because consumers are *willing to pay* (WTP) different prices for each marginal (additional) unit of output up to Q^*. The investment cost of the project is C, the area under the supply (or marginal cost) curve. Hence, from a public sector perspective, the project is desirable if $A + B > C$.

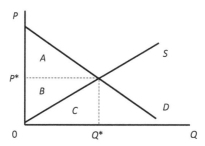

Fig. 3.2   Project benefit.

If the private sector evaluates the project, the revenue is $B + C$ and the cost is C. The profit is B, and the rate of profit is B/C. The firm does not consider area A, the consumers' surplus, and under-estimates the social benefit. In practice, firms will also try to capture the consumers' surplus if they can differentiate high-paying and low-paying customers (Nagle and Muller, 2017). For example, airlines charge different prices for business class, first class, and economy seats. For our present purpose, we shall assume that there is no differentiation of users for public projects. Everyone pays the same price, such as for electricity, water, or road usage.

How do we know if social welfare has improved? In the Pareto criterion, a project improves social welfare if at least one person is better off, and no one is worse off. It is impractical because almost every project has winners and losers. Hence, CBA uses the *Kaldor-Hicks criterion* where social welfare has improved if benefits exceed costs and winners can potentially compensate losers. The compensation is only potential; it may not occur. For example, in a road project, the government is likely to compensate residents for land acquisition but not for noise and dust. Further, the cost of acquisition may encourage public agencies to acquire land in the poorer areas of the city for public projects.

The steps in CBA are:

- identification and valuation of benefits;
- identification and valuation of costs;
- computation of net present value (NPV) and internal rate of return (IRR);
- risk assessment; and
- recommendation.

We discuss these steps below, followed by criticisms of CBA.

Project benefits

There are three possible benefits in a project, namely,

- output benefit, such as electricity or water;
- cost reduction, such as transport savings; and
- external benefits, such as an improvement in the environment.

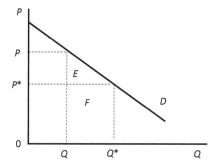

Fig. 3.3   Output benefit for a power generation project.

We discuss each benefit below.

(a) Output benefit

The output benefit is the area under the demand curve (Fig. 3.3). The current industry electricity output is Q, and project output is $Q^* - Q = q$. The additional output causes the price to fall from P to P^*. The project benefit is the area $E + F$, the social willingness to pay for the benefit.

If the price fall is negligible, then E is small and we can neglect it. The project benefit is then F, that is, the revenue. If the price fall is large, we need to estimate the price elasticity of demand using the standard formula

$$e = (\% \text{ change in quantity demanded})/(\% \text{ change in price}).$$

Rearranging,

$$\% \text{ change in price} = [(q/Q) \times 100]/e.$$

Once we know e, P, Q and q, it is possible to find P^* and then use it to estimate $E + F$. The value of e is estimated from previous econometric studies, such as for electricity consumption (Shu and Hyndman, 2011). P and Q are the existing industry price and output respectively, and Q^* is $Q + q$.

(b) Cost reduction

The direct benefit of a transport project, such as an upgraded road, consists of cost reductions or savings. For existing commuters making Q (round) trips a year, the cost of travel (including road toll) falls from C to C^* (Fig. 3.4). The benefit is the area X through savings in

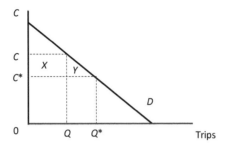

Fig. 3.4   Benefit for transport project.

- travel time;
- vehicle operating cost;
- injury cost; and
- property damage.

A second benefit is area *Y*, which represents the gain to

- new commuters who now travel because of the lower cost (generated traffic); and
- existing commuters diverted from elsewhere in the city.

The total benefit of the project is *X* + *Y*.

There may be other short-term benefits, such as reduced congestion in other parts of the city because of the diversion. There may be other costs as well; for example, the upgraded road may transfer congestion to another part of the city. We assume these effects are small or they cancel out. There may also be longer-term indirect benefits such as those that affect the quality of life. We ignore these benefits because they are often difficult to estimate and uncertain. A further reason is that, when discounted to present value at a relatively high discount rate, distant benefits are much smaller than short-term ones.

As before, the estimation of *X* and *Y* requires knowledge of the demand curve. In the short run, commuters driving to work are relatively insensitive to price changes (Goodwin *et al.*, 2004). However, unlike Fig. 3.3, it is difficult to estimate *Q**, which is why road toll projects are risky for investors.

(c) External benefits

Finally, a project may generate external benefits. For example, the external benefits of a road project include

- increase in the output of another industry;
- worker training;
- technology adoption by other firms;
- alleviation of poverty;
- employment and income multiplier effects;
- rise in property prices;
- creation of new businesses; and
- improvement in environmental quality.

An upgraded road may stimulate additional farm production because of better access to rural markets. The benefit is the additional farm output multiplied by individual prices, that is,

$$\text{Benefit of additional farm output} = \Sigma\, p_i Q_i$$

over n farm products.

A project may involve worker training or the adoption of new technology by other firms or projects. It may also alleviate poverty by improving access to schools, employment, and better facilities. These benefits are either hard to estimate or often regarded as small. It is also difficult to derive distributional weights to give the poor greater consideration in evaluating projects.

A project benefits the local community by creating new jobs. If there is full employment in the country, the project does not generate additional jobs. Instead, it will need to offer higher wages to attract workers from other sectors. In a recession, a project may not generate many new jobs because most firms have excess capacity and do not need to hire new workers. Another reason for the slower hiring is possible mismatch of skills or lack of experience on the part of new workers. The construction industry tends to lose experienced workers during a recession. When the boom returns after a long period, workers who have left the industry may not return. This constant need to train new workers to replace the departing experienced workers is probably a reason for the lower productivity in construction.

By employing new workers, a project creates successive rounds of spending. However, there are income leakages out of the local economy through central government taxes, imports, and repayment of debt. Debt repayment is a major reason why government spending may not increase private consumption; instead of spending the additional income, households use it to repay debt.

Taken together, these employment and income multiplier effects are probably not large (Bom and Ligthart, 2014; Stupak, 2018). They also depend on the type of investment, with industrial facilities having greater impact than social infrastructure such as housing. The effects are greater during recessions.

A road project is likely to raise property prices along the route. However, this merely capitalizes transport cost savings, resulting in double counting. Hence, we ignore the rise in property prices. Similarly, a new road that bypasses a town may create new businesses along its route and destroy existing businesses in town. Despite the disruptions, the net effect may be negligible.

A project may improve the environment quality, such as better air quality by reducing congestion. Since there are no directly observable market prices for air quality, we need to estimate *shadow prices* for the benefit. In *contingent valuation* (Mitchell and Carson, 1989), we survey the affected community's willingness to pay (WTP) for the benefit. From a representative sample, it is possible to compute the average annual WTP and then multiply it by the size of the affected population to obtain the aggregate WTP. However, respondents may not be able to answer hypothetical questions about the environment. A question like "How much are you willing to pay each year for a 10 percent improvement in air quality?" is not easy to answer. A second problem with contingent valuation is that respondents may under-declare their WTP to reduce their contributions if the project goes ahead. This is the classic *free-rider problem* in the provision of public goods. Conversely, respondents may also over-declare the desirability of a project if they know that the government will provide a substantial subsidy.

Project costs

The project costs consist of direct input costs and indirect external costs. The direct input costs consists of "hard costs" comprising land, capital, labor, materials, transport costs, and utilities as well as "soft costs" such as professional fees, statutory approvals, and permits. These inputs are valued at competitive prices to reflect the real resource costs. Transfer payments such as profit, interest, subsidies, levies, and taxes do not involve real resources and are excluded from project costs in CBA.

If monopoly, price controls, subsidies, and taxes distort domestic prices for local goods, we need to adjust them to competitive market levels. These adjustments can be complex because of theoretical and data issues. A more practical approach is to use market prices unless the distortions are large. Some projects involve donors and in-kind donations, if any, must be valued at resource cost.

For tradeable goods, we use international prices to value imported inputs, including insurance, freight, and local transport costs. Import duties are excluded. Obviously, international products have differing quality and functionality, and hence different prices. There is usually no single textbook "competitive" price. It is common for the same product to be sold at varying prices in different countries. If the official exchange rate (OER) is not competitive, it is necessary to use a shadow exchange rate (SER) to convert world prices in another currency to domestic prices. Some governments deliberately over-value their currencies to cheapen the import of equipment and materials for industrialization, at the expense of agriculture and other exports. In such cases, the OER will not be competitive. Finally, if the project exports tradable goods, government subsidies to promote exports are excluded from project costs.

For capital cost, the investment is booked at historic cost rather than the commercial practice of depreciating it annually. The commercial practice avoids reflecting a major loss in the first year of operation because of the large initial investment. For CBA, there is no need to spread the initial capital cost over a number of years.

The labor market may not be in equilibrium because of minimum wage legislation, union power, discrimination, and other reasons. If the project hires skilled workers and professionals, the market wage rate, including employment benefits, approximates the opportunity cost of labor. For unskilled labor, there are two possibilities. If the project uses rural or migrant workers, the opportunity cost is the rural wage rate. If the project employs urban workers, the opportunity cost is the urban wage rate.

For utilities, it is possible that the provider is a monopolist or public company. Many governments in the developing world subsidize utilities and, if so, we need to adjust the rates to competitive levels. The adjustment is not crucial if utilities make up only a small portion of project cost.

A project may generate external costs. To estimate such costs, we may use

- loss of output;
- loss of worker earnings;
- replacement or restoration cost;
- averting expenses;
- medical expenses;
- the price difference in two projects "with and without" the external cost;
- surrogate markets; and
- contingent valuation.

If a firm pollutes a river, it results in loss of output for fishermen. In transport projects, the loss of earnings may be used to estimate the time cost of congestion. This is called the *human capital approach*. If a project results in soil erosion, we may value the external cost by computing the cost of restoration. If a house is next to a noisy road, the owner may install double-glazed windows, which are averting expenses. In pollution studies, one may use the medical expenses of the affected community to estimate the cost of air pollution. The estimates are incremental, that is, on "with and without project" basis to compare the two options. The "without project" option is business as usual.

The housing market can act as a *surrogate market* for road noise because house buyers consider its adverse effect on property values. This is called the *revealed preference approach* because we use actual human behavior to estimate shadow prices. All else equal, a house facing a noisy road will sell less than a quieter one. This is the principle of *hedonic pricing* (Rosen, 1974), where the price of a house depends on its bundle of characteristics such as accessibility, land area, built-up area, tenure, age, type of construction, orientation, noise, amenities, and so on. Each characteristic has an unobservable "implicit" price. We can use regression analysis to estimate implicit prices using

$$P_i = f(C, N; \beta), \qquad i = 1, \ldots, n.$$

Here, P_i is the price of the ith house, $f(.)$ is a regression function, C is a vector of house characteristics except noise, N is noise, $\boldsymbol{\beta}$ is a vector of k coefficients, and n is the sample size. For a linear function,

$$P_i = \beta_1 + \beta_2 A_i + \cdots + \beta_k N_i + \varepsilon_i$$

where A_i is the age of the house and so on, and ε_i is the error term with zero mean. The expected (mean) value is

$$E(P_i) = \beta_1 + \beta_2 A_i + \cdots + \beta_k N_i.$$

Our interest is the value of β_k. Partial differentiation of $E(.)$ with respect to N gives

$$\partial E(P_i)/\ \partial N_i = \beta_k.$$

Hence, β_k is the average house price change for each unit change in noise level (in decibels), holding other house characteristics constant. A simpler approach is to make N_i a dummy variable where $N_i = 1$ if a house is noisy and 0 if it is not. Then β_k is the estimated average price difference between a noisy and a quiet house, holding all other housing characteristics constant.

In practice, we use about 10 to 15 house characteristics such as age, design, land area, built-up area, orientation, number of rooms, accessibility, and so on. Hence, the sample must be reasonably large (e.g., $n = 300$ transacted house sales) to obtain reliable estimates of the coefficients (Tan, 2018).

The housing market must be stable to avoid large price errors, which implies that transacted house sales should be within a short period, such as three months. Further, note that noise affects buyers of expensive houses more than purchasers of cheaper houses. Hedonic price estimates of the benefit of noise reduction around airports puts it at about one percent per decibel (Nelson, 1980). Thus, if the desired reduction is five decibels, it will raise nearby property values by about five percent.

The final method of valuing the external cost of a project is *contingent valuation*, that is, we ask affected residents for their *willingness to accept* (WTA) compensation for the environmental *deterioration*. Recall that we can use WTP to value environmental *improvement*. In general, for a given level of improvement or a similar level of deterioration, WTA is greater than WTP because people tend to value a loss more than a similar gain. Contingent valuation has some weaknesses. First, the values will vary across different races, income groups, educational levels, degrees of risk aversion, and so on. Second, the questionnaire design may affect the responses because of emotive reactions towards environmental changes. Finally, some people are unwilling to accept compensation for destroying nature because it is priceless.

Computation of net present value and internal rate of return

The benefits (B_t) and costs (C_t) of a project accrue over the project life and need to be discounted to net present value (NPV), that is,

$$NPV = \Sigma \ (B_t - C_t)/(1 + r)^t. \tag{3.1}$$

Here r is the *discount rate*, t is time, and the summation is over all periods (i.e. annually) from $t = 0$ to $t = n$, the project terminal period (e.g. 25 years). Whether t starts from 0 or 1 is a matter of assumption as long as there is consistency. In discounting future benefits and costs, we assume that they occur at the end of each period, rather than at the start or middle of the period (year). A project is economically feasible if $NPV > 0$. We can also rank projects using the NPV criterion.

It is simpler to discount *real* benefits and costs. This obviates the need to guess future rates of inflation in estimating B_t and C_t. Hence, the discount rate is also real. The link between real and nominal rates is given by

$$1 + r = (1 + R)/(1 + \pi)$$

where r is the real discount rate, R is the nominal discount rate, and π is the expected rate of inflation. Rearranging,

$$1 + R = (1 + r)(1 + \pi) = 1 + \pi + r + r\pi.$$

For small values of r and π, $r\pi$ is close to 0. Hence,

$$r = R - \pi.$$

That is, the real rate is the nominal rate minus the expected rate of inflation. For example, if the bank quotes a savings deposit rate of 2% and the expected rate of inflation is 1.5%, the real interest rate is 0.5%.

What should be the real discount rate (r) in evaluating projects? The general formula is

$$r = \text{WACC} + \lambda.$$

WACC is the weighted average cost of capital, and λ is the risk premium. Suppose the government funds a project using the following means:

Source of funds	Amount ($m)	Proportion of project cost	Cost of funds (%)
Tax	20	0.20	5
Bond	30	0.30	6
Loan	50	0.50	8
	$100 m	1.00	

Then

$$\text{WACC} = 0.20(5\%) + 0.30(6\%) + 0.50(8\%) = 6.8\%.$$

If a project is riskier than normal, it is usual to add a *risk premium* (λ) to the WACC to reflect the higher risk. An objection to this approach is that risks have been incorporated into the cost of funds. However, lenders and bondholders may not be fully aware of the risks. Many governments use a real discount rate of about 3%, and slightly lower for $n > 30$ years so that distant benefits and costs do not become negligible. Instead of the government's cost of funds, some analysts use the market interest rates for savings and loans. These two rates differ because the lender needs to make money. There are valid arguments for using either rates. Analysts who are in support of using the savings rate argue that it better reflects the social rate of time preference. The market lending rate reflects the private sector's cost of funds.

Instead of searching for a discount rate to use in the NPV formula, we may compute the project IRR k by setting $NPV = 0$ and solving for k:

$$0 = \Sigma \, (B_t - C_t)/(1 + k)^t. \tag{3.2}$$

Example: Computation of IRR

Suppose a project has the following benefits and costs:

t	Benefit ($m)	Cost ($m)	$B_t - C_t$
0	0	100	−100
1	40	10	30
2	50	10	40
3	60	10	50

Then, using a 5% discount rate,

$$NPV = \Sigma \, (B_t - C_t)/(1 + r)^t$$
$$= -100 + 30/(1.05) + 40/(1.05)^2 + 50/(1.05)^3 = \$8.1 \text{ m.}$$

To find the project IRR, we solve

$$0 = -100 + 30/(1 + k) + 40/(1+ k)^2 + 50/(1+ k)^3$$

by varying k until the value on the right-hand side (RHS) is close to 0:

k	RHS
0.08	0.18
0.09	−0.02
0.089	0

Hence, the project IRR is 8.9%, which is higher than the 5% discount rate. In practice, it is easier to use free software to compute the IRR. Note that it is possible to have multiple roots if there are alternating cash flows. However, this is rare for infrastructure projects. Generally, the project incurs costs during the pre-construction and construction stages and generates benefits during operation.

We compare the project IRR with the hurdle rate, the government's minimum required rate of return. In many cases, the hurdle rate is the WACC. Like the NPV criterion, we may also use the IRR to rank projects.

Example: Cost-benefit analysis of a proposed road project

We now consider a simple example of CBA to put all the elements together. A proposed road-upgrading project has the following costs and benefits ($m):

	Year			
	0	1–4	5–29	30
Benefits	0	0	3.2	3.2
Costs				
Land	−100	0	0	100
Construction	0	−50	0	0
Operation and Maintenance	0	0	−1	−1
Noise	0	0	−1	−1
Net benefit	−100	−50	1.2	101.2

Inflows are booked as positive and outflows are negative. The benefits include

- annual travel cost savings computed using Fig. 3.3;
- annual fall in road fatalities, by multiplying the number of lives saved by estimates of future earnings less consumption expenditure; and
- improvement in air quality, estimated using contingent valuation.

The construction period covers Years 1 to 4, and the column figures are construction expenses ($50 m) for a typical year of construction. The operation phase is from Years 5 to 30 and the column figures are for a typical year to avoid too many columns.

By using real benefits and costs, there is no need to adjust the values for annual inflation. In the terminal year (Year 30), the land reverts and its value is booked as positive ($100 m). Hence,

$$NPV = -100 - 50/(1+r) + \cdots + 1.2/(1+r)^5 + \cdots + 101.2/(1+r)^{30}.$$

To compute the project IRR, we set $NPV = 0$ and replace r with k. The computation is left as an exercise. You should use hand computation to get a feel of the mechanics and check your answer using free IRR software.

Risk assessment

There are many ways to assess project risks, including

- sensitivity analysis;
- Monte Carlo simulation (MCS);
- risk-adjusted discount rate;
- project options; and
- qualitative method.

In sensitivity analysis, we investigate how *NPV* changes if we alter *one* variable and hold other variables constant. The most popular choice is to change the discount rate, such as using 3%, 6% and 9% respectively and see how *NPV* varies.

In MCS, we use random numbers to change the variables *simultaneously* to see how *NPV* changes. The popular choices are the discount rate, revenue, and initial investment cost (Table 3.2). The second and third columns show the possible values of each variable and the subjective probability distribution respectively. The values and probabilities are derived from experience. The next column gives the cumulative probabilities, which must sum to unity. Finally, we assign corresponding numbers between 00 and 99 based on the cumulative probabilities.

Table 3.2   Logic of Monte Carlo simulation.

Variables	Possible values	Probability distribution	Cumulative probability	Assigned numbers
Discount rate	5%	0.3	0.3	0–29
	7%	0.5	0.8	30–79
	9%	0.2	1.0	80–99
Revenue	$45 m	0.2	0.2	0–19
	$40 m	0.7	0.9	20–89
	$35 m	0.1	1.0	90–99
Initial cost	$95 m	0.2	0.2	0–19
	$100 m	0.6	0.8	20–79
	$105 m	0.2	1.0	80–99

In each trial, we draw three random numbers between 00 and 99, similar to the casinos in Monte Carlo. For example, if the first trial draws the set (25, 65, 10), it corresponds to (5%, $40 m, $95 m) in the table. We use these three values to compute the first *NPV*, assuming that the revenue of $40 m is the same for each year. If the second trial draws the set (80, 4, 35), it corresponds to (9%, $45 m, $100 m). We use these values to compute the second *NPV*, and so on.

By using a large number of trials, we can develop frequency tables and use them to compute the mean and standard deviation of *NPV*. The latter is a measure of project risk from simultaneous changes in the three variables. If desired, other variables such as input costs may be included.

There are many software on MCS, such as the @Risk add-in function in Microsoft EXCEL. Some versions allow correlation among the variables, which is more realistic than assuming independence. For example, if the project is completed during a recession, the revenues for the initial years may be low and we may want to use a lower discount rate instead of a randomly selected one.

Another method of dealing with risk is to use a risk-adjusted discount rate so that

$$NPV = \Sigma \, (B_t - C_t)/(1 + r^*)^t.$$

Here $r^* = r + \lambda$ where, as before, λ is the risk premium. Recall that it is common practice to set r = WACC and add a risk premium for riskier projects. A different argument is that $\lambda = 0$ because the public sector has a large portfolio of projects to spread the risk (Arrow and Lind, 1970).

A project may contain *real options* such as the option to expand if a project shows subsequent promise, or the option to scale down or abandon it if demand is much lower than expected. The option is "real" in the sense that it consumes physical resources, as opposed to financial options.

Suppose a project has three periods, Year 0, Year 1, and Year 2 (Fig. 3.5). The boxes represent *NPV*s (in $m) rather than profit to obviate the need to discount cash flows to present value. In Year 1, the project has a 0.8 chance of earning $70 m and a 0.2 chance of losing $10 m by decommissioning it. The *NPV* for Year 0 is 0.8(70) + 0.2(−10) = $54 m. In Year 1, the *NPV* is 0.6(90) + 0.4(40) = $70 m. In short, we work backwards to compute the *NPV* for each period.

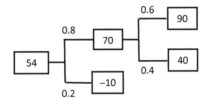

Fig. 3.5   Project with real options.

The final and most common technique is qualitative risk assessment. The *commercial risks* of a project include

- *completion risks*, where the project fails to achieve the time, cost, safety, and quality targets;
- *market risks*, that is, insufficient revenue because of price or volume, high input costs, or non-payment by buyers;
- *operation and maintenance risks* relating to equipment failure, inefficient operation, and input supply issues;
- *financial risks* relating to movements in foreign exchange, inflation, and interest rates;
- *social and environmental risks* relating to heritage, resettlement, illegal or unhealthy work practices, perceived lack of participation by affected parties, and environmental damage; and
- *force majeure risks* such as war, civil unrest, general strikes, epidemics, and natural disasters that directly destroy the project assets or indirectly disrupt its supply chain.

The *non-commercial risks* include

- *political risks* through acts of government such as change in government, nationalization, expropriation, issues with permits and approvals, inability to repatriate profit, restrictions on operation, and general instabilities such as war and civil unrest; and
- *regulatory risks* including change in law, protection of property rights, and dispute resolution.

There appears to be some overlap between political and force majeure risks. However, unlike force majeure events, political events arise through deliberate government action.

Risk assessment involves ascertaining the likelihood (L) of a risk event and its impact (I). Risk exposure is the product $L \times I$, as shown in the risk assessment matrix for non-commercial risks in Table 3.3. The

Table 3.3   Risk assessment matrix for non-commercial risks.

Risk	Likelihood (L)	Impact (I)	Exposure ($L \times I$)	Mitigation
Political				Political risk insurance,
Tax changes	1	1	1	Implementation Agreement
Social opposition	3	4	12	(if possible), involve local
Terrorism	1	4	4	sponsor and multilateral development agencies in
Expropriation	1	5	5	financing
Repatriation of profit	1	5	5	
Production restrictions	1	5	5	
Trade restrictions	1	5	5	
Corruption	3	4	12	
Regulatory				Develop PPP framework, seek
Regulatory framework	1	3	3	legal advice, contractual allocation of risks
Permits	1	3	3	
Change in regulation	2	3	6	
Legal framework	1	3	3	
Disputes	5	4	20	
Changes in law	1	1	1	
Environmental				Resettlement plan, community
Opposition	3	4	12	participation and inclusion, Environmental Impact
Damage	1	3	3	Assessment, mitigation, and insurance against clean-up cost
Force majeure (FM)	1	5	5	Insurance, FM provisions in PPP contract
Land acquisition	4	5	20	Land Acquisition Act, stakeholder management
End of concession	5	3	15	Link final payment to asset condition in PPP contract

scoring is based on a 1–5 rating scale with higher scores representing greater likelihood and impact.

In general, risk is allocated to the party that is best able to manage it. Hence, the grantor assumes the non-commercial risks while the SPV manages the commercial risks. If both parties have no control over the risk event, such as a natural disaster, they should share the risk.

A party may mitigate project risks by

- avoiding it, that is, not to initiate or bid for the project at the expense of future benefits or profits;
- transferring it to another party, through risk allocation or insurance;
- retaining it, if the risk is manageable; and
- reducing it, through contracts, hedging, and other means.

Specific risk mitigation strategies for commercial risks arising from market failure are shown in Table 3.4.

During the implementation stage, there is a need to monitor the risks as they may change or new risks may appear. Periodically, there should be a major risk review after each project milestone.

Table 3.4   Mitigation strategies for risks from market failure.

Market failure	Mitigation
Monopoly	Competition
Public good	Institutions to overcome collective action problems
Externality	Regulation, tax, cap and trade system, define and assign property rights, and private bargaining
Imperfect information	
Hidden information	Specifications, screen, test, measure, external review, track record, warranties, certification, and advertising
Hidden effort	Incentives, penalties, supervision, appeal to values (culture), and indoctrination
Hidden action	Excess (in insurance), vertical integration, long-term fixed contracts, diversify sources
Hidden future	Hedging instruments, predictive models, insurance

Recommendation

The final step in CBA is to recommend whether the project is economically feasible. Note the analysis is purely economic, and the final approval will need to take into account technical, financial, political, and other considerations.

Criticisms of cost-benefit analysis

There are many criticisms of CBA. First, there may be political interference in the process to influence the decision so that project selection is not just a technical matter for engineers and economists (Pressman and Wildavsky, 1979). A project affects many stakeholders such as international donors, politicians, bureaucrats, lenders, businesses, farmers, social activists, and residents. Each group will try to influence the outcome.

Second, there are considerable difficulties in valuing benefits and costs, particularly those involving shadow prices where data are harder to collect. The demand curve, willingness to pay for a good or service, and willingness to accept compensation for a deterioration of the environment depend on income. Consequently, the distribution of income in society influences preferences.

Third, the process may exclude certain stakeholders such as the poor, future generations, and those who are adversely affected or displaced by the project. Institutional reform is necessary to include these marginalized communities when evaluating and implementing projects (Mishra and Prasad, 2020).

Fourth, as we have seen, there are differing opinions on the choice of discount rate. A different value of the discount rate will affect the net present value and hence the decision whether the project is economically viable.

Fifth, the government may not compensate losers or the compensation is inadequate. This is especially so in relation to land acquisition because the process is costly. Consequently, the land acquisition process is a sensitive issue and may turn violent (Sathe, 2017). An adequate compensation is necessary if displaced landowners are to become partners in the development process.

Finally, the use of market values often results in public acquisition of cheaper land from poorer areas of the city. This will displace the working classes unless there are alternative housing and business establishments. It is even cheaper to clear slums or squatters as part of urban renewal (O'Conner, 1995).

Despite these and other criticisms, CBA is still widely used for the evaluation of public projects for lack of a suitable alternative.

Political, regulatory, and legal assessment

A project may generate political support or opposition. Those who oppose it are likely to cite land acquisition, environmental concerns, user afford-ability, excessive costs, and insufficient benefits. The project will also need to meet regulatory requirements and assessed for potential legal issues, particularly in countries with weak regulatory frameworks and legal systems.

For PPP projects, an assessment of bankability is required. A project is bankable if it can attract commercial lending. It may be possible to provide some government support or change the terms of the PPP con-tract, such as to lengthen the concession period, to improve bankability.

Business case

The business or policy case sums up the preliminary study.

Traditionally, a project is considered "successful" if it is delivered to specifications, completed on time, and is within budget. However, it may still be a white elephant. Hence, it is necessary to provide the business or policy case, which considers the value of the project to stakeholders (Thoradeniya and Tan, 2018).

For commercial projects, the business case is likely to be

- profit;
- process improvement;
- strategic; or
- compliance with regulatory requirements.

The strategy may be an expansion into a new market, launch of a new product, or investment to deter the entry of competitors.

For public projects, the high-level policy case at this stage may be value for money as discussed earlier under the section on technical assessment. The contents of the policy case include

- background;
- project definition;
- project governance structure;
- technical feasibility;
- economic feasibility;
- financials;
- project delivery;
- procurement; and
- risk management.

Observe that the policy case contains the key points of a preliminary study.

References

Arrow, K. and Lind, R. (1970) Uncertainty and the evaluation of public investments. *American Economic Review*, 60(3), 364–378.

Bom, P. and Ligthart, J. (2014) What have we learned from three decades of research on the productivity of public capital? *Journal of Economic Surveys*, 28(5), 889–916.

Derman, W. and Whiteford, S. (2019) *Social impact analysis and development planning in the Third World*. London: Routledge.

Drummond, M., Sculpher, M., Claxton, K., Stoddart, G., and Torrance, G. (1997) *Methods for economic evaluation of health care programmes*. London: Oxford University Press.

Goodwin, P., Dargay, J., and Hanly, M. (2004) Elasticities of road traffic and fuel consumption with respect to price and income: A review. *Transport Reviews*, 24(3), 275–292.

Hebbar, K. (1991) *Integrated rural development program*. New Delhi: Deep and Deep.

Levy, J. (1995) *Essential microeconomics for public policy analysis*. New York: Prager.

Mishra, S. and Prasad, S. (Eds.) (2020) *Displacement, impoverishment, and exclusion.* London: Routledge.

Mitchell, R. and Carson, R. (1989) *Using surveys to value public goods: The contingent valuation method.* New York: Resources for the Future.

Nagle, T. and Muller, G. (2017) *The strategy and tactics of pricing.* London: Routledge.

Nelson, J. (1980) Airports and property values: A survey of recent evidence. *Journal of Transport Economics and Policy*, 14(1), 37–52.

O'Conner, T. (1995) *Building a new Boston: Politics and urban renewal, 1950–70.* Boston: Northeastern University Press.

Pressman, J. and Wildavsky, A. (1979) *Implementation.* Berkeley: University of California Press.

Rosen, S. (1974) Hedonic prices and implicit markets: Product differentiation in pure competition. *Journal of Political Economy*, 82(1), 34–55.

Sathe, D. (2017) *The political economy of land acquisition in India.* London: Palgrave Macmillan.

Shu, F. and Hyndman, R. (2011) The price elasticity of electricity demand in South Australia. *Energy Policy*, 39(6), 3709–3719.

Stupak, J. (2018) *Economic impact of infrastructure investment.* Washington DC: Congressional Research Service 7–5700, R44896.

Tan, W. (2018) *Research methods: A practical guide for students and researchers.* S'pore: World Scientific.

Thoradeniya, D. and Tan, W. (2018) Strategic value of a Chinese-funded infrastructure project in Sri Lanka. *Infrastructure Asset Management*, 7(2), 127–133.

World Bank (2019) *Policy guidelines for managing unsolicited proposals in infrastructure projects.* Washington DC: World Bank.

CHAPTER 4

Feasibility study

Project brief

If the high-level business case developed from the preliminary study is approved, the next step in the infrastructure development cycle is to proceed to a more detailed feasibility study. The first thing to do in this phase is for the grantor to develop the Project Brief as the basis for briefing the project team before embarking on the feasibility study. Depending on the capacity of the grantor, it may be necessary to appoint external consultants to assist with the feasibility study. If new issues surface during the preliminary study, the grantor will also gather additional inputs from stakeholders.

The Project Brief contains the following information:

- background;
- basic development options;
- preferred option;
- project benefits;
- project output and basic specifications;
- site, including constraints and opportunities;
- basic engineering and design options;
- sustainability and resilient considerations;
- preliminary schedule and milestones;
- revenues and costs;
- stakeholders;
- socio-environmental impacts and mitigation strategies;
- choice of delivery;
- procurement strategy;

- project governance structure;
- regulatory requirements; and
- management of risks.

The list is not exhaustive. It can be tailored to suit different types of infrastructure projects.

Feasibility study

For Public Private Partnership (PPP) projects, it is the special purpose vehicle (SPV) that finances, designs, builds, operates, and maintains the facility. Hence, the grantor's feasibility study covers the following areas:

- output and technology specifications;
- site analysis;
- site appraisal;
- project schedule, milestones, and length of concession period;
- development of the shadow bid;
- political feasibility and user affordability;
- fiscal sustainability;
- regulatory and legal assessment;
- economic feasibility;
- socio-environmental impacts and mitigation strategies;
- PPP contract structure;
- project governance structure;
- bankability; and
- possible government support.

We discuss these elements below. Many of these items have been covered in the preliminary study. At this stage, it is necessary to confirm some issues, such as economic feasibility, and go deeper into others, such as site analysis. For practical reasons, it is not necessary to cover every aspect of the feasibility study in detail. Rather, we focus on the most salient features. However, do bear in mind that what appears to be minor at this stage may cause major problems during implementation.

Output and technology

The grantor needs to specify the output and technology without over-constraining how the SPV may deliver the product or service. For example, in the case of power generation, the grantor may specify the output and the use of a gas-fired plant.

It is prudent to build in some technological or output flexibility because of the long concession period. For example, a facility may contain "white" spaces for future use, areas for physical expansion, convertible spaces, and possible changes from non-renewable to renewable technologies.

Generally, there is a preference among lenders and grantors for tried and tested technology to minimize the risk of failure. In some cases, grantors deliberately specify the use of a new technology for political, strategic, or commercial reasons.

Site analysis

For infrastructure projects that are procured using PPP, the grantor normally acquires the site and leases it to the SPV. Alternatively, the grantor may arrange for the SPV to lease it from another public entity, which is often the land authority.

Site analysis refers to assessments of the legal, physical, built-up, external, and social aspects of the site. These factors affect the value of a site, and hence the cost of land acquisition for the project.

The legal aspects of a site include the boundary, ownership, title, tenure, covenants, regulatory requirements, property tax obligations, performance obligations, and possible development charge or fee. Land titles may include covenants to preserve the character of the neighborhood, such as the permissible use of certain designs or types of construction materials. The planning authority may impose performance obligations as part of planning approval, such as the need to provide a park or walkway. Finally, a development charge (or fee) is applicable if there are changes to permissible land use or density of development. The charge is levied as a percentage of the change in land value to encourage redevelopment of the site.

The physical characteristics of a site include its size, shape, topography, drainage, vegetation, geology, and soil. These features present constraints and possibilities, including size of project, scenic views, shading, potential flooding, type of foundation, and possible land contamination.

The built-up features include improvements such as existing buildings, utilities, heritage or conserved structures, roads, and other structures.

A site has many external features such as

- accessibility to major centers and transport modes;
- surrounding land uses and amenities such as schools, parks, and markets;
- undesirable features such as if it is next to a slum; and
- environmental qualities such as traffic, noise, wind, air, snow, and sun.

Depending on the type of project, it may be necessary to consider the ease of movement during construction as well as for project outputs and inputs such as materials, fuel, labor, plant, and equipment.

The social aspects of a site concern stakeholders, neighbors, land acquisition, possible resettlement, employment changes, possible environment damage, traffic, and other community issues.

Following a site analysis, the grantor may consider land use options and configurations, including the development of a site master plan. If it is a small site, this task may be left to the private sector.

Site appraisal

Site appraisal is necessary to determine the rent of the site or cost of land acquisition. For Build-Operate-Transfer (BOT) projects, the most common arrangement is for the SPV to lease the site from the grantor or the land authority for the length of the concession period. At the end of this period, the asset and land revert to the government.

The government may acquire a single site or many sites along a proposed railway line or highway. These sites may be appraised using comparable property sales data in the vicinity and checked using rental data. The latter is called the income approach to value, that is,

$$V = R/k$$

where V is the capital value of the asset (e.g., a house), R is the current annual gross rent, and k is the gross capitalization rate (e.g., 4%). If the net rent is used, then k is the net capitalization rate. To "capitalize" means to convert the rent into capital or asset value, in this case by multiplying it by $(1/k)$. We often use the gross rent because the information is more readily available than net rent. The net rent is computed by deducting maintenance, repairs, property tax, insurance, and other expenses from the gross rent. The market capitalization rate is obtained from sales data, that is, by computing R/V for similar properties preferably, but not necessarily, in the neighborhood. The assumption is that the rate of return is competitive across different asset classes after adjusting for risks. For example, investing in office buildings should yield similar returns after adjusting for site and other differences.

For private development projects, the developer will need to purchase or lease the land if she is not the owner. The value of the land (L) can be estimated using comparable land sales but because development projects tend to be large and unique, there may not be comparable land sales in the vicinity. A more common approach is to compute L as a residual by deducting initial building cost (C), interest expense during construction (I), sales and letting costs (S) and developer's profit (π) from the capitalized revenue, or gross development value (GDV). For example, for an office building,

$$L = GDV - C - I - S - \pi.$$

Here,

$$GDV = R/k$$

where R is the current annual gross rental income and k is the market capitalization rate. Recall that this is the income approach to value. The building cost consists of the hard costs of site preparation and construction as well as the soft costs comprising professional, planning approval, funding, legal, and other fees (Cadman and Topping, 1995). The computation is set out in a table:

Rental income	R
Capitalization rate	k
Gross development value	$GDV = R/k$

Building cost

Construction cost

Site investigation and preparation

Fees

    Professional fees

    Planning and other fees

    Funding fees

    Legal fees

    Other fees

Total building cost C

Interest expense I

Sales and letting costs S

Developer's profit π

Land value $L = GDV - C - I - S - \pi$

    The developer pays interest on land, building cost, and fees as part of the development loan. The interest is payable on the disbursed amount of loan over the development period (e.g. 5 years), which can be tricky to compute. Many analysts simplify the computation of interest by using simple interest over half the development period. Similarly, they estimate some of the fees as a percentage of construction cost. Hence, the residual method of estimating L is only approximate because it is based on forecasts of future revenues and rough estimates of costs. Property development is a risky business (McNellis, 2016), and property cycles can be volatile (Grenadier, 1995).

    Before a private developer purchases a potential site, he normally buys an option from the seller to keep it from the market. The option premium is about 1% of the agreed purchase price and the period is usually about three to six months for the developer to conduct his feasibility study, secure financing, and obtain in-principle town planning approval. If the project is not feasible, the option expires worthless and the developer loses the premium. If the project looks promising, the premium becomes part of the down payment for the purchase of land. Other methods of acquiring land for private development include government land sales, joint development with the landowner, and using a long-term ground lease.

Project schedule, milestones, and length of concession period

At the feasibility stage, the grantor's construction schedule is approximate and largely based on past experience. It is usual to break up a large project into different phases as project milestones.

The length of the concession period should allow the SPV to make an adequate return based on the shadow bid model. It is possible to use a variable concession period based on target revenue, net present value, or return on investment. The SPV may seek to renegotiate the length of the concession period if there are unpredicted risks that lead to a substantial fall in revenue, such as the COVID-19 pandemic.

Shadow bid model

The shadow bid model serves as a guide to compare bids. Generally, these bids will need to cover

- debt service and return to equity;
- fixed operation and maintenance expenses; and
- variable costs such as fuel and electricity.

There may be other payments such as electricity generated in waste-to-energy plants. For some projects such as sports facilities, the grantor and SPV may share the revenue.

There are often periodic reviews of tariffs and fees to adjust for demand changes, inflation, fluctuations in input prices, and currency movements. For energy-intensive projects such as electricity generation and desalination, there is often a pass-through mechanism to shift the risk of fluctuating input prices from the SPV to the user or off-taker.

For projects in developing countries, the tariff may allow for currency adjustments if the SPV borrows in a stable foreign currency (e.g. US$) but revenues are in a less stable local currency.

Political feasibility and user affordability

Political feasibility and user affordability have already been covered during the preliminary study. These issues will be revisited if there are major changes such as the emergence of new stakeholders.

Fiscal sustainability

Fiscal sustainability refers to the grantor's ability to make periodic payments under the PPP contract until the end of the concession period. If the project charges user fees and there is a public subsidy, the government must be able to continue to provide the subsidy and compensate users for the higher fees if there are tariff adjustments.

Many countries have relatively independent central banks to conduct monetary policy but few countries have similar institutional arrangements for the conduct of fiscal policy. Further, there is no consensus on the level of public debt relative to Gross Domestic Product (GDP). The third complication is that the public debt may refer to the debt of the central government or all levels of government, and may include the debt of State-owned enterprises guaranteed by the government. We also compare the size of the debt to the country's growth potential.

Regulatory and legal assessment

The grantor needs to assess the clarity of legal contract clauses, regulatory design and quality, extent of public liability, and enforcement of contracts. Of importance is the need to streamline complex procedures, facilitate the approval of permits and approvals, and address conflicting legislation. Clearly, the grantor needs to seek legal and other opinions on many of these issues.

Socio-environmental impacts and mitigation strategies

Recall that, in the preliminary study, the grantor carries out an economic feasibility study that includes assessment of external benefits and costs. These assessments are economic rather than technical.

At the feasibility study stage, there is a need to conduct in-depth studies on social concerns such as land acquisition and resettlement. The environmental concerns include sustainability of resources, pollution, conservation of culture and heritage, and loss of habitat and biodiversity.

There are two phases in an environmental impact study. Phase I is common for infrastructure projects and, if major issues crop up, there is a more detailed Phase II investigation and proposed mitigation measures.

In terms of ecologically sustainable development, the possible adverse impacts include (O'Hara, 2014)

- removal of trees;
- destruction of soil structure and soil contamination;
- increase in rainfall run-off because of hard surfaces;
- barriers to the use of adjoining land by the community because of disamenities;
- air, water, land, light, and noise pollution;
- hazardous wastes;
- loss of habitats;
- degradation of surrounding environment;
- loss of biodiversity;
- obstruction to movement of animals;
- pressure on water supplies and other infrastructure (Hedberg, 2020);
- reduction in urban resilience, such as to floods (Coaffee and Lee, 2016); and
- pollution from use of non-renewable energy sources.

There may be positive impacts from infrastructure development, and these impacts may arise by reversing the negative impacts above. For example, it may replant rather than remove trees.

The mitigation of these adverse impacts requires an effective policy, regulatory, and tax framework. The policy framework requires the adoption of appropriate social and environmental policies. The regulatory framework requires the effective exercise of planning, development, as well as environmental assessments and controls when approving projects. In particular, projects should incorporate sustainable and resilient designs (see Chapter 1) and adopt green construction materials and methods. Finally, governments may use tax and other incentives to encourage sustainable and resilient practices.

Mitigation requires ongoing evaluation of policy, regulation, and tax regimes. The social and environmental impacts will need to be closely monitored so that remedial actions may be undertaken.

Public Private Partnership contract structure

The basic PPP contract structure is BOT. There are variations, such as Build-Operate-Own (BOO) if the asset has little residual value to transfer at the end of the concession period.

In a Build-Transfer-Operate (BTO) project, the transfer of asset takes place after the construction phase and the grantor then gives the SPV the right to operate the facility during the concession period. In general, in PPP contract structures, the government owns the asset and gives the SPV the right of operation. In some cases, such as in BOO projects, the SPV owns the asset.

The risk allocation follows the principles discussed in Chapter 3. The grantor manages non-commercial risks, and the SPV handles commercial risks. Both parties should share risks beyond their control.

Project governance structure

The project governance structure spells out the decision-making authority, that is, who decides in the project. A large infrastructure project may involve different ministries and hence there is a need to set up a steering committee comprising senior bureaucrats to oversee the project. Often, the senior official from the Ministry of Finance or primary ministry heads this committee.

Bankability

A project is bankable if it is able to attract private lending. The grantor's assessment of bankability considers whether the project makes commercial sense to entice sponsors to bid for it.

If the project is not bankable, the grantor may consider changing the terms of the contract and possible government support to make it bankable. For example, it may consider lengthening the concession period.

Possible government support

If a project is not bankable on its own strength, the possible government support includes (Irwin, 2003)

- capital grant or subsidy;
- tax incentives;
- equity participation;
- guarantees; and
- building of connecting and ancillary facilities.

For example, the government may provide a guarantee against the default of a public entity as an off-taker or input supplier. The support may also be non-financial, such as by helping to win community support for the project (Stein, 1992).

Market sounding

As part of the feasibility study, the grantor sounds the market about six months to a year before tender (depending on the complexity of the project) to gather feedback and gauge private sector interest.

Market sounding should not be too early when the project is still in its early stage of design because the feedback will be vague. Conversely, it should not be too late, such as when the design is already fixed.

The feedback should be from industry networks and not from particular firms to avoid perceptions of partiality. The grantor gathers information about output specifications, market conditions, technologies and costs, payment mechanism, and risk allocation from the key stakeholders.

The feedback may take the form of written comments, survey responses, or interviews based on the circulated project information memorandum.

Example: Market sounding for Waste to Energy (WTE) project in Maldives (January, 2019)

This open market sounding exercise, by the Ministry of Environment (MOE), sought to obtain public feedback. In 2016 and 2017, MOE completed the concept design and feasibility study for a regional waste management facility (RWMF) in Thilafushi.

The key stakeholders are the Ministry of Finance (executing agency), MOE (implementing agency), a government-owned firm (Waste Management Corporation Ltd) that currently runs the waste collection, the State Electricity Company (potential off-taker), the Environmental Protection Agency, and Greater Malé Industrial Zone Ltd (GMIZL), the regional industrial development entity.

The RWMF will consist of a harbor and reception area for reception of waste, a construction and demolition waste (CDW) processing plant, an end-of-life vehicle dismantling unit, a WTE plant, a bottom ash processing plant, leachate storage and treatment facilities, and a seawater inlet and outlet structure. MOE will conduct studies to determine the demand for CDW, bottom ash, and recyclables.

The market sounding notice provided information on the site and its constraints, type of contract (Design, Build, and Operate (DBO)), contract form and risk allocation (FIDIC DBO contract), main characteristics of the WTE plant, anticipated waste composition, qualification criteria for bidders, and broad project schedule. The proposed payment terms and mechanism include monthly fixed and variable fees, asset replacement reimbursement according to contractor's bid price schedule, and adjustment for inflation and exchange rate movements. Both parties will share the revenue from sale of electricity.

MOE is particularly interested in obtaining feedback on the geotechnical and environmental risks of building the WTE plant on a newly reclaimed island on a coral reef.

Business case

Recall from the previous chapter that a high-level business case follows from a preliminary study to determine if the project should proceed to the feasibility study stage. Likewise, a business case is required after the feasibility study to seek approval on whether the project should go ahead.

The format of the business case follows the items in the feasibility study with clear justifications in support of the project.

References

Cadman, D. and Topping, R. (1995) *Property development*. London: Routledge.

Coaffee, J. and Lee, P. (2016) *Urban resilience*. New York: Springer.

Grenadier, S. (1995) The persistence of real estate cycles. *Journal of Real Estate Finance and Economics*, 10(2), 95–119.

Hedberg, T. (2020) *The environmental impact of overpopulation*. London: Routledge.

Irwin, T. (2003) *Public money for private infrastructure*. Washington DC: World Bank.

McNellis, J. (2016) *Making it in real estate*. Washington DC: Urban Land Institute.

O'Hara, K. (2014) *Earth resources and environmental impacts*. New York: Wiley.

Stein, D. (1992) *Winning community support for land use projects*. Washington DC: Urban Land Institute.

CHAPTER 5

Project preparation

Preparation of documents

As part of project preparation, the grantor prepares the following tender and other documents:

- Request for Qualification;
- draft Public Private Partnership (PPP) contract;
- draft permits and approvals;
- Request for Proposal;
- Instructions to bidders; and
- Response Package.

We discuss these documents below.

Request for Qualification

The Request for Qualification (RFQ), also called Invitation for Expressions of Interest, is part of the grantor's initial screening process. The RFQ stipulates the project scope of works and invites potential bidders to respond.

Firms that respond to the RFQ will be evaluated on the qualifying criteria. The usual criteria include financial capacity, technical expertise, project experience, details of key project team members, list of major plant and equipment (if relevant), record of disputes, and recommendation letters.

Some governments may impose additional criteria such as domestic project experience, inclusive participation, labor rights (Corvaglia, 2020), sustainable procurement (Addis and Talbot, 2001), and the use of local contractors and operators.

Normally, grantors use a "points system" based on the above criteria to shortlist potential bidders. The weights depend on the grantor's priority. It is possible to use pairwise comparisons among the criteria to derive the weights (Saaty, 1980). Ultimately, the weights are derived from subjective judgments. For example, suppose there are four criteria, namely, financial resources (*F*), technical expertise (*T*), experience (*E*), and other factors (*O*). The first step is to make pairwise comparisons to obtain the following table:

	F	*T*	*E*	*O*
F	1	**4**	3	5
T	**1/4**	1	2	4
E	1/3	1/2	1	3
O	1/5	1/4	1/3	1

For example, if we decide that *F* is 4 times more important than *T*, then the (*F*, *T*) cell is given the value 4, as shown in boldface font. The (*T*, *F*) cell is then given the inverse of 4, which is 1/4. By proceeding this way for other pairwise comparisons, we have the complete table as shown.

The next step is to normalize the cell values by dividing each element by its column sum to obtain

	F	*T*	*E*	*O*	Weightage
F	0.56	0.70	0.47	0.38	0.53
T	0.14	0.17	0.32	0.31	0.23
E	0.19	0.09	0.16	0.23	0.17
O	0.11	0.04	0.05	0.08	0.07

The weightage in the final column is the row average. We may round off the weights as 50%, 25%, 15%, and 10% respectively.

Draft Public Private Partnership contract

The draft PPP contract will depend on whether the grantor provides a concession, is an off-taker, or supplies the input. It may contain the following:

- obligations of the grantor;
- obligations of the special purpose vehicle (SPV);
- fee mechanism;
- safety and environmental requirements;
- force majeure arrangements;
- restrictions on transfer of shares by SPV;
- applicable legal and tax rules;
- step-in rights;
- dispute resolution; and
- possible assignment of benefits to lender.

The obligations of the grantor may include

- grant of exclusive concession to the SPV for the stipulated period;
- site acquisition;
- facilitation, provision or approval of permits and approvals;
- environmental assessments;
- enabling legislation;
- building of connecting and ancillary services;
- guarantees and tax concessions;
- fuel supply and purchase of output;
- possible compensation to SPV for certain risks (e.g. change in law);
- the right of the SPV to terminate the project with compensation on default of grantor; and
- supervision and monitoring of progress.

The obligations of the SPV may include

- taking over of site from the grantor;
- financing, design, and building of the facility to specification by a certain date;
- meeting output quality and volume;
- entering into off-take purchase contract or input contract;
- meeting maintenance standards with penalties for poor performance;
- allowing for early termination with compensation or upon default;
- training of grantor's workforce before transfer of asset; and
- ensuring satisfactory asset condition at the end of contract period.

The grantor needs to seek legal opinion in drafting the PPP contract.

Draft permits and approvals

The grantor prepares draft permits and approvals that are often distributed as part of the tender documents. These documents concern town planning, building, traffic, safety, health, hazardous waste, pollution, and other environmental issues.

Request for Proposal

The Request for Proposal (RFP), or Invitation to Tender, provides information on project goals and objectives, project features, procurement strategy, draft contract, copies of permits and approvals, technical information, bid instructions, evaluation criteria, and instructions on how the grantor will handle queries from potential bidders.

Instructions to bidders

These instructions assist bidders on how to respond to the RFP. They may include submission requirements, cost of submission, permissible language to use, closing date, withdrawal and modifications of offers, clarification procedure, tender deposit, validity of offer, no obligation for grantor to award contract, confidentiality of information, conflict of interest, corrupt practices (Guraka, 2016), handling of bid errors, and protests.

Response Package

The Response Package is a formal submission format for the tender, for example,

- bidder's particulars;
- price proposal;
- design proposal;
- declaration of non-collusion;
- tender deposit;
- in-principle financing support; and
- proposed contractor, key subcontractors, operator, and suppliers.

CHAPTER 5 | Project preparation   **65**

At this stage, a bidder may not know the identity of proposed contractor. The bidder may be a consortium comprising the contractor, operator, and other shareholders.

Land acquisition

If the project requires a site that the grantor does not own, the final step in project preparation is site acquisition.

Even if there is a Land Acquisition Act to acquire land for public purposes, this can be a tedious and long-drawn affair over its alleged public purpose, trust, transparency, efficiency of the process, clarity of land ownership, and fair compensation (Chakravorty, 2013). Within the public sector, it may also not be easy to acquire land from other ministries and agencies (Pressman and Wildavsky, 1979). Hence, land acquisition has to start early so as not to delay the project.

References

Addis, B. and Talbot, R. (2001) *Sustainable construction procurement*. London: CIRIA.

Chakravorty, S. (2013) *The price of land: Acquisition, conflict, consequence*. London: Oxford University Press.

Corvaglia, M. (2020) *Public procurement and labor rights*. Portland, Oregon: Hart Publishing.

Guraka, E. (2016) *Politics of favoritism in public procurement in Turkey*. London: Palgrave Macmillan.

Pressman, J. and Wildavsky, A. (1979) *Implementation*. Berkeley: University of California Press.

Saaty, T. (1980) *The analytic hierarchy process*. New York: McGraw-Hill.

CHAPTER 6

Tender

Pre-qualifying bidders

After project preparation has been completed, the next stage is for the grantor to invite potential bidders to express their interests and pre-qualify for the project by responding to the Request for Qualification (RFQ). Grantors do not use open tenders for Public Private Partnership (PPP) projects because of their size, high cost of bid preparation, and complexity. In an open tender, there is no pre-qualification and any firm can bid for the project. If a project is sensitive, such as a military installation, the grantor may use a limited tender by inviting only one or two firms to bid. It is also possible to negotiate directly with the firms.

As discussed in the previous chapter, it is common for grantors to use a points system to shortlist about four to eight bidders in a selective tender. The weights will depend on the nature of the project and the grantor's priorities (Bauccio-Teschlog *et al.*, 2020). For example, in technically complex projects, project experience and technical capacity will be given greater weight. Preparing for a PPP tender is costly and time-consuming. Hence, beyond eight bidders, the probability of winning is too small to encourage active participation. It may draw risky bidders.

Request for Proposal

After shortlisting, potential bidders will be asked to respond to the Request for Proposal (RFP). For a PPP project, this stage may last up to a year or more depending on the complexity of the project.

Bidders are likely to form consortiums to share risks, expertise, and resources. They will need to provide separate design and price proposals. At this stage, the design is conceptual or preliminary. Finally, bidders will often need to develop the business case to secure in-principle financing approval. The next chapter will cover how tenderers prepare their bids by performing these tasks.

Responding to queries

During the bidding period, the grantor will respond to queries and clarifications from bidders, sometimes called the *market feedback period*, not to be confused with market sounding during the feasibility study.

Bidders will provide their feedback and queries as well as those from potential lenders. For example, lenders may express certain concerns that affect bankability or make suggestions to improve it. They may also be uncomfortable with certain contract clauses.

There is often a pre-bid meeting or briefing for potential bidders near the site, and it is followed by a site visit.

Issue of final tender

The grantor will incorporate the relevant feedback from shortlisted bidders and other stakeholders before issuing the final tender.

Alternatively, there is no feedback period or issue of final tender. The grantor issues the tender documents to shortlisted bidders for their responses. However, because infrastructure projects tend to be complex, it is good practice to have a feedback period and issuance of final tender.

Tender deposit

The tender deposit or bid bond ensures that bidders will honor their bids. It is to cover the loss if the winning bidder decides not to proceed with the project and the grantor has to award the contract to another bidder. A winning bidder may walk away from the project for various reasons, such as the withdrawal of a co-sponsor, major bid errors, or the perceived inability to secure higher debt financing.

The bidder purchases the bid bond from the surety or bonding company. The penal sum is the amount the bond will cover, which is usually 5 to 10 percent of the bid amount but it can be as high as 20 percent.

It is the estimated price difference between the winning bid and the second bid. The surety conducts extensive checks on the bidder before agreeing to provide the bond.

The bond premium is about one to five percent of the penal sum depending on the size of the project and reputation of the bidder (Russell, 1999).

References

Bauccio-Teschlog, T., Carney, D., Foster, J., King, R., and Weber, C. (2020) *Developing and managing Requests for Proposals in the public sector.* London: Routledge.

Russell, J. (1999) *Surety bonds for construction contracts.* Virginia: ASCE.

CHAPTER 7

Sponsor's bid preparation

Decision to tender

In the previous chapter, we discussed how the grantor shortlists potential bidders and issues the Request for Proposal (RFP). Bidders will respond to the RFP by first providing input during the market feedback period and attending the pre-bid meeting and site visit. Thereafter, the grantor will issue the final tender after considering the feedback.

A sponsor's decision to tender depends on

- expected profitability;
- bankability;
- the size, uniqueness, and prestige of the project;
- likelihood of finding co-sponsors, local partners, and other investors to share the risks as well as financial and other resources;
- current workload and project schedule;
- time required for bidding;
- cost of bidding;
- transparency of the tender process;
- number of bidders;
- reputation of the grantor, for example, as off-taker;
- commercial risks; and
- non-commercial risks relating to political, regulatory, social, and legal issues.

Sponsors sign a Development Agreement among themselves on how to proceed. If they subsequently secure the project contract, the agreement forms the basis to develop the Shareholders' Agreement.

Development agreement

The agreement will spell out the basic rules of collaboration, such as the establishment of a study team, how to determine the design and price proposals as responses to the grantor's RFP, funding of pre-development activities, and the subsequent shareholding structure and management of the SPV or project company. The special purpose vehicle (SPV) is established after contract award and financial close.

Project team

Sponsors may have their own project and design team, or they may hire external consultants based on expertise, experience, proposed fee and other criteria such as knowledge of local conditions. At this stage, the grantor has not awarded the contract and the sponsor will want to minimize bid preparation costs, which is about 0.5 to 1.5 percent of bid (KPMG, 2010).

The project team for large infrastructure projects typically consists of senior members with extensive expertise and experience. There are clear roles and responsibilities in the project governance structure. The team regulates their relations by contract, builds trust with internal and external stakeholders, and learns to get along. It also develops internal and external coalitions to get things done.

Design proposal

The design proposal is guided by aspirational and functional objectives. The aspirational aspects may include new technologies, methods, benchmarks, designs, and uses for the site. The grantor is likely to provide the development concept in the tender brief without over-constraining how bidders will respond.

Depending on the type of project, the functional items include the scope and size of the project, types of spaces, integration, flexibility, energy efficiency, sustainability, and so on. These items are found in the tender specifications. For example, a high-speed rail (HSR) system consists of the following components:

- infrastructure;
- rolling stock (trains); and
- operation and maintenance.

The infrastructure includes the route layout, civil works, stations, depots, track geometry, power supply, and signaling system. Train operation and maintenance includes timetabling, scheduling, ticketing, maintenance, and repairs. The grantor is likely to award separate contracts to private contractors to build the infrastructure because of the scale and complexity of the project. Similarly, the stations, depots, power supply and signaling system can be unbundled into separate contracts. There may be a single or separate operation and maintenance contracts.

Route planning requires information on expected ridership based on locals and tourists. Once the tentative stations and routes have been selected based on demand studies, the grantor will conduct preliminary engineering studies, often by appointing external consultants. These studies normally include an environmental impact assessment (EIA), the layout of existing rail lines for possible coordination and integration with the proposed HSR, the topography, and geology. Using such information, the grantor evaluates the possible routes using benefits, costs, environmental, social, and other criteria. Thereafter, geotechnical investigations can begin to finalize the route.

If there are separate operation and maintenance contracts, then the SPV as operator needs to submit proposed designs for timetable, schedule, ticketing, and so on. At the tender stage, the design is conceptual or schematic. It breaks the system into components and their respective narratives. As the design progressives, there will be progressive cost estimates as a basis for the price proposal.

Price proposal

The price proposal concerns profitability, that is, the project is commercially viable and hence able to attract financing, that is, it is bankable.

The profitability of a project depends on many factors. These components are discussed below.

Political, regulatory, and legal assessments

In Chapters 3 and 4, we discussed how the government assessed the political, regulatory, and legal risks. The SPV carries out a similar assessment from a different perspective. These risks to the SPV include

- interference in the project;
- revocation of contract;
- confiscation of assets;
- non-payment as off-taker;
- new regulatory requirements;
- weak enforcement of contracts and dispute resolution mechanisms;
- disruption in supplies;
- forced participation by State-owned enterprises;
- non-approval of permits and licenses;
- change in tax;
- trade curbs;
- corruption;
- deliberate delays;
- renegotiation of contract on less favorable terms; and
- currency controls.

There are ways to mitigate these risks, such as by signing a government support agreement on the above, borrowing from international multilateral banks to discourage governments from predatory behavior, and use of appropriate contract clauses such as international arbitration.

Revenue

Sponsors can mitigate demand risks by

- conducting a proper market study;
- using "take or pay" purchase contracts;
- using financial options;
- seeking creditworthy buyers; and
- ensuring that the product meets quality standards.

We discuss the first three methods below.

Market study

A market study is used to estimate revenue, that is, output demand and price. Demand depends on demographics, price, income, availability of substitutes, and policy variables such as taxation and exchange rates.

The price depends on demand and supply. On the supply side, competitors may react through price and non-price competition. For non-durable goods, the demand and supply curves determine price. For durable goods, we use the *stock-flow model*, as shown below, for short-term forecasting. For longer-term projections, we need to study demographic, income, and other trends.

Example: Stock-flow model of the housing market

The demand for private housing units (D_t) depends on price and other non-price demand "shifters" such as the rate of household formation, household income, credit conditions (e.g. loan to value ratio), mortgage interest rate, prices of substitutes (e.g. public or rental housing), exchange rates (for foreign buyers), and policy variables such as taxes, stamp duty, and housing regulations. The demand curve is a function of price only, and changes in non-price variables shift the demand curve, that is,

$$D_t = f(P_t, \mathbf{x}_{t-s})$$

where P_t is house price at time t, $f(.)$ is usually a linear or log-linear function, and $\mathbf{x}_{t-s}$ is a vector of the shifters. Generally, $\mathbf{x}_{t-s}$ contains current and lagged variables because the sale and purchase of a house is a long process. For example, buyers arrange their financing about one quarter prior to actual sale, and the relevant mortgage interest rate (r) should be lagged by one period if one uses quarterly data, that is, r_{t-1}. There may be another quarter of lag between a sale and lodgment of caveat.

The supply of housing units (S_t) in any period consists of the previous stock (S_{t-1}) and newly completed units (C_t) so that

$$S_t = (1 - \lambda)S_{t-1} + C_t.$$

Here λ is the annual rate of physical depreciation, which is about 2% or 0.02 for residential buildings. In addition, the supply of housing units includes additions (renovations) and losses through demolitions, floods, and fire. The standard assumption is that these effects cancel out.

The supply of new units (C_t) depends largely on the actions of housing developers, that is,

$$C_t = g(P_{t-k}, \mathbf{y}_{t-k})$$

where $g(.)$ is the linear or log-linear supply function, P is house price as before, and $\mathbf{y}$ is a vector of supply shifters such as land cost, construction cost, interest rates, and policy variables that affect housing supply, for example, developer's stamp duty and development charge. Because housing construction takes time, developers make their decision to build about one to three years earlier, which explains the presence of lag k. For example, if there is a lag of one year, $k = 1$. Developers build on forward-looking expectation that houses are sellable in future.

We need specify the market condition, that is, whether it is in equilibrium or disequilibrium. Disequilibrium models are more complicated and many housing models assume market equilibrium so that

$$D_t = S_t.$$

We solve for house price by substituting the previous three questions into the equilibrium condition, giving

$$P_t = h(P_{t-k}, \mathbf{x}_{t-s}, \mathbf{y}_{t-k}).$$

Usually, $h(.)$ is assumed to be linear or log-linear so that it can be estimated using linear regression (Tan, 2018). The estimated model may then be used to study and forecast house price movements. If desired, it is possible to specify a disequilibrium model by allowing price changes to adjust depending on the lagged vacancy rate (V_{t-1}) and prices plus a random term (ε), that is,

$$\Delta P_t = \alpha + \beta V_{t-1} + \phi \, \Delta P_{t-1} + \varepsilon_t$$

where α is the intercept and β, ϕ are parameters. There are many variants of such disequilibrium adjustments.

The model requires substantial amounts of data because of the large number of variables over many periods. Some of the data may not be available, up to date, or accurate. To estimate these equations, the time series must be stationary; otherwise, first differencing is required for each non-stationary variable. Finally, note that the model is for short-term forecasts only. For long-term forecasts, it is common to use long-term growth rates of key variables based on historic trends.

Purchase contract

Sponsors may also mitigate demand risk by using "take or pay" purchase contracts specifying minimum quantities and prices. That is, the purchaser must pay a penalty even if he does not take delivery of the output.

Such contracts are common in the energy sector because of the high initial investment. Without such a contract to guarantee a minimum volume of sales, the investment may be too risky for the seller.

Financial options

Another way to mitigate demand risk is to use call and put options, as explained in the examples below.

Example: Call option

A call option allows the holder the right to *buy* an asset in future at a specified price at the expiry or exercise date. For example, a developer may wish to purchase a piece of land for development for $100,000 (the exercise price). The landowner sells the developer a call option for $2,000 (the premium) to keep the land from the market for three months for her to conduct feasibility study and arrange financing. On the expiry date, the developer may exercise the option and pay the remaining $98,000 or forgo the $2,000 if the project is not feasible.

There are variations from this basic call option, such as the ability of exercise at any time (an American option) rather than only at expiry, which is a European option. Option pricing refers to methods of ascertaining the premium, which depends on expectations of the value of the asset at expiry, the duration of the option period, the exercise price, and the time value of money.

As illustrated above, call options are used in projects to purchase inputs such as land, fuel, and raw materials.

Example: Put option

A put option is an option to *sell* an asset in future at a specific price. Hence, the primary use of a put option is to sell the project output.

Suppose the above landowner is migrating and wishes to sell the land in three months for $110,000. He manages to buy a put option from an investor for $3,000. The investor receives $3,000. If the landowner decides to sell the land in three months, the investor will pay the remaining $107,000. However, if land prices spike, the landowner will not exercise the option and loses $3,000. He will sell the land in the open market at a higher price. However, if land prices slide, the landowner will exercise the option. Obviously, the investor is thinking that land prices will go up if he enters into a put contract.

One line of research in option pricing is to determine the premium given the current stock price, strike price, time to expiry, and volatility. We now discuss one such method, the Black-Scholes model (see McDonald, 2014).

The volatility of a stock is the standard deviation of the rate of return on stock prices. For example, if we have annual stock prices (S), then the rate of return for any year is

$$r_t = (S_t - S_{t-1})/S_{t-1}.$$

If we have 20 annual rates of return, the volatility (σ) is its standard deviation. Note it is the standard deviation of the rate of return and not the share price.

The Black-Scholes model assumes stock prices (S) move in continuous time (t) according to the *Geometric Brownian Movement* (GBM), that is,

$$dS = \mu S dt + \sigma S dz. \tag{7.1}$$

Here,

$$dz = \varepsilon \sqrt{(dt)}, \quad \varepsilon \sim N(0, 1).$$

It follows the *Wiener process* or Standard Brownian Movement (SBM). In discrete time, it is called a *random walk* and is given by

$$z_t = z_{t-1} + \varepsilon_t.$$

More generally, we can write Equation (7.1) as

$$dS = adt + bdz. \qquad (7.2)$$

Here a and b are functions of S and t. For example, comparing Equations (7.1) and (7.2), $a = \mu S$ and $b = \sigma S$. Note that S and dz are functions of t, and the time subscripts are omitted to avoid clutter. Before deriving the Black-Scholes model, we need Ito's lemma.

Ito's lemma:

If $f = f(S, t)$ and S fluctuates according to Equation (7.2), then

$$df = (a\ \partial f/\partial S + \partial f/\partial t + \tfrac{1}{2}\ b^2\ \partial^2 f/\partial S^2)dt + b\ \partial f/\partial S\ dz.$$

The proof is based on Taylor's expansion of $f = f(S, t)$, that is,

$$df = \partial f/\partial S\ dS + \partial f/\partial t\ dt + \tfrac{1}{2}\ \partial^2 f/\partial S^2\ (dS)^2$$

Substituting for dS from Equation (7.2),

$$df = \partial f/\partial S\ (adt + bdz) + \partial f/\partial t\ dt + \tfrac{1}{2}\ \partial^2 f/\partial S^2\ (adt + bdz)^2$$
$$= (\partial f/\partial S\ a + \partial f/\partial t + \tfrac{1}{2}\ \partial^2 f/\partial S^2\ b^2)dt + \partial f/\partial S\ bdz.$$

To get the second line, we use the following results:

- $dz = \varepsilon\sqrt{(dt)}$, so $(dz)^2 = \varepsilon^2 dt = dt$ because $E(\varepsilon^2) = 1$, that is, the expected value of a chi-square variable equals its degree of freedom; and
- $(dt)^2 = dtdz = 0$ for small increments dt and dz.

This completes the proof.

We are now ready to derive the Black-Scholes model. Let $C(S, t)$ be the value of a call option on S. Then, using Equation (7.1) and Ito's lemma,

$$dC = (\mu S \partial C/\partial S + \partial C/\partial t + \tfrac{1}{2}\ \sigma^2 S^2 \partial^2 C/\partial S^2)dt + \sigma S\ \partial C/\partial S\ dz. \quad (7.3)$$

If we hold a portfolio comprising x units of bond and y units of stock, its value is

$$P = xB + yS. \qquad (7.4)$$

Hence,

$$dP = xdB + ydS.$$

All variables in the above portfolio equation are functions of time. If we invest in a bond at constant risk-free interest rate r, the instantaneous return is

$$dB = rBdt.$$

To understand this expression, rewrite it as

$$dB/B = rdt.$$

Integrating both sides gives

$$B = B_0 e^{rt}$$

where B_0 is the value of the bond at time $t = 0$, and e is the base of natural logarithm.

Substituting for dB in the portfolio equation, we get

$$dP = xrBdt + y(\mu Sdt + \sigma Sdz) = (rxB + y\mu S)dt + y\sigma Sdz. \qquad (7.5)$$

If we make the value of the call option equal to the replicating portfolio, $dC = dP$. Hence, equating Equations (7.3) and (7.5) gives

$$y = \partial C/\partial S; \text{ and}$$

$$x = \{\partial C/\partial t + \tfrac{1}{2}\, \sigma^2 S^2 \partial^2 C/\partial S^2\}/(rB).$$

Substituting x and y into Equation (7.4) and setting $P = C$, we obtain the Black-Scholes partial differential equation (PDE)

$$rS\, \partial C/\partial S + \partial C/\partial t + \tfrac{1}{2}\, \sigma^2 S^2\, \partial^2 C/\partial S^2 = rC. \qquad (7.6)$$

The solution to this PDE is

$$C = SN(d_1) - Ke^{-rT}N(d_2) \qquad (7.7)$$

where

$$d_1 = \{\log(S/K) + (r + 0.5\sigma^2)T\}/(\sigma\sqrt{T}); \text{ and}$$
$$d_2 = d_1 - \sigma\sqrt{T}.$$

Here, $N(z)$ is the shaded area under the standard normal curve from negative infinity to z and T is the time to expiry, in years. As before, r is the risk-free interest rate, σ is the volatility of the price series S, and log(.) stands for natural logarithm.

As shown in the example below, we first compute d_1 and d_2 and use these values to find $N(d_1)$ and $N(d_2)$ by looking up the standard normal distribution table. Finally, we compute C using Equation (7.7).

Example: Pricing of call option

The current land price (S) is $100 per m². If the strike price K is $105 per m² with a $T = 2$ year expiry, price the call if the risk-free interest rate (r) is 0.04 and the volatility (σ) is 0.2.

Solution:

$$d_1 = \{\log(100/105) + (0.04 + 0.5(0.2)^2)2\}/(0.2\sqrt{2}) = 0.251; \text{ and}$$
$$d_2 = 0.251 - 0.2\sqrt{2} = -0.032.$$

From the standard normal statistical table, $N(0.251) = 0.599$, and $N(-0.032) = 0.488$. Hence,

$$C = 100(0.599) - 105e^{-0.04(2)}(0.488) = \$12.60.$$

Note this is a European option, that is, it is exercised only at expiry. For an American option that can be exercised at any time, valuing the call is more complicated (Joshi, 2010).

Procurement strategy

Similar to that of the grantor, a sponsor's procurement strategy consists of three elements, namely,

- ways of sourcing for contractors;
- project delivery methods; and
- payment methods.

As discussed in Chapter 3, there are three ways to source for contractors, namely, open, selective, and limited tender. Sponsors tend to use competitive selective tender. For project delivery methods (see Table 3.1), the most common methods are traditional Design-Bid-Build (DBB) or Design-Build (DB) contract, which is similar to the Engineering, Procurement and Construction (EPC) contract in the process industry.

Generally, project lenders prefer fixed price contracts to lock in the project cost. It requires the SPV to exercise tight control on costs.

Cost estimates

Sponsors tend to use per unit basis to estimate project costs from the preliminary design. The estimates include

- the hard cost of facilities;
- contingency of about 5 to 10 percent of construction cost depending on the nature of project;
- soft costs comprising professional fees, permits, and other development fees;
- working capital;
- interior furnishings;
- periodic capital investment; and
- interest payable during construction.

Often, lenders will roll over the interest during construction and include it as part of the loan amount.

Schedule estimate

Sponsors will also estimate the schedule using a bar chart comprising the pre-construction, construction, and post-construction activities. At this stage, the schedule is preliminary and relies primarily on experience in executing similar projects.

The pre-construction activities include feasibility study, preparing and bidding for the PPP contract, project design, securing early regulatory approvals, developing the construction procurement strategy, and mobilizing resources for construction.

The construction activities consist of achieving major milestones such as the completion of major building components, commissioning of major systems, training of operatives, and occupation.

Finally, the post-construction period include testing, calibration, rectification of defects, and ramp-up towards full operational capacity.

Quality

Sponsors control project quality through a quality plan that includes specifications, quality assurance of processes, quality control, retention sum, and warranties against defects. The measures are incorporated into the construction contract. The retention sum is about 10 percent of the monthly progress payment up to a limit of five percent of the contract sum.

Similarly, the contractor is, by contract, required to furnish a quality plan for sponsor's approval. Part of the plan concerns how the contractor selects and monitors subcontractors to ensure quality.

Construction

The contractor may not perform in terms of time, cost, quality, and safety. Hence, the procurement strategy and choice of contractor are important considerations. In addition, sponsors use incentives and penalties such as early completion bonus, performance bond, warranties, and liquidated damages to motivate the contractor. The performance bond should cover any extension of time and the defects liability period. Its value will need to be adjusted if there are major contract variations.

Sponsors need to put in place a rigorous method of project management and control to avoid scope creep, delays, cost escalations, claims, and costly disputes.

The contractor will be required, by contract, to furnish and implement a construction safety plan.

Inputs

A project requires inputs such as raw materials, product components, energy, and utilities. Input supplies require site access.

Generally, the SPV will enter into *forward purchase contracts* to secure certain input supplies at fixed prices. The SPV may enter into such supply contracts for only a portion of the project input needs so that it can also benefit by buying from the open market if market prices fall below the fixed contract price.

Alternatively, it may purchase a call option to buy a certain quantity of the input at a fixed price in future. Recall that a call option gives the holder the right, but not the obligation, of exercise before or at expiry.

Another hedging strategy is to diversify input sources to ensure prices are competitive and reduce supply disruptions.

Operation and maintenance

Many things can go wrong during the operation and maintenance (O and M) phase, which is the longest period of a project's life cycle. There are two main risks, namely, failure to perform, and inefficiency.

Clearly, having an experienced operator helps, particularly if he is also motivated by his equity commitment in the project. However, having the operator as an equity investor poses possible conflict of interest. Hence, there is a need for performance incentives and penalties for poor performance.

Generally, sponsors and lenders prefer tried and tested technology. If the project uses a new technology, the SPV must secure a guarantee from the technology supplier. Other equipment may also fail, and a warranty is necessary. It is also possible to enter into a maintenance agreement with the manufacturer.

Finally, facilities managers and operatives require training by experienced facilities managers, equipment suppliers, and technical experts.

Force majeure events

There are three forms of force majeure (FM) risks, namely,

- political and social unrest such as wars, strikes, and civil unrest;
- change in law; and
- natural disasters and other events (e.g., explosion and pandemic).

In general, the SPV is excused from contractual performance for political FM and change in law, and *may* be entitled to time extension and compensation by the grantor depending on the terms of the contract. However, it needs to cover other FM risks through insurance.

Sources and cost of funds

Sources of funds

Sponsors often finance their projects with equity and debt. Although sponsors provide "equity," they usually provide subordinated or shareholders' loans that are often treated as equity. Instead of receiving dividends, they receive interest payments which the SPV can book to reduce its tax. Passive investors may provide equity or purchase convertible debt, that is, it is convertible to equity if the project is successful.

To get the best deal, sponsors invite lenders to bid for the loan package. These lenders form a syndicate among themselves to share the loan and reduce their exposure to risks. These senior bank loans have priority for claims over shareholder loans if the SPV defaults or goes bankrupt.

In some countries, such as the US, another institutional lender may "take out" the construction loan during the operation phase. This mechanism requires the permanent lender to issue a commitment letter to the sponsor and construction lender. There are two reasons for this arrangement. First, the construction lender does not want to lend on long-term basis to reduce the mismatch between the short-term nature of its savings deposits and long-term lending. Second, the permanent lender such as an insurer that invests in the long term to match its insurance policies does not want to handle the construction risk.

During the operation phase, it is possible to refinance the loan because interest rates may have fallen or there is no longer any construction risk. With lower risks, borrowing rates should come down. The refinancing may be through another bank loan or by issuing a bond. The latter is more complicated because the SPV has to deal with many different investors, issuance costs and procedures, greater disclosure, and subsequent difficulties in adjusting financing terms and covenants.

Other sources of funds include

- export credit agencies that provide loans related to the export of their countries' equipment to the project;
- short-term supplier credit;
- passive investors such as infrastructure investment funds, pension funds, and insurance companies;
- government grants as a catalyst to encourage participation by private investors;
- carbon credits;
- multilateral development agencies such as the World Bank or Asian Development Bank; and
- Islamic finance.

The World Bank's Multilateral Investment Guarantee Agency (MIGA) also provides political risk insurance, partial credit guarantee to cover the sovereign borrower's non-payment of debt in public projects, and partial risk guarantee to cover non-performance of sovereign contractual obligations.

Islamic finance differs from conventional loans. Financing is based on Islamic laws that prohibit the payment or receipt of interest and lending for certain activities such as gambling and alcohol. The lender provides a loan and, instead of interest payments, it takes a share of the profit. Since it is possible for the borrower not to earn a profit, the lender effectively shares the risks.

Islamic finance is an important source of funds for projects in countries not well served by conventional project finance. A project may also be jointly funded by conventional and Islamic finance.

Cost of funds

Recall from Chapter 3 that the weighted cost of capital (WACC) is given by

$$\text{WACC} = (1 - \lambda)r_e + \lambda (1 - t)r_d.$$

Here λ is the fraction of debt, r_e is the cost of equity, r_d is the cost of debt, and t is the corporate tax rate (e.g. 0.25). For example, if a project uses 30% equity and 70% debt, then $\lambda = 0.7$. Generally, interest expense on debt is tax deductible, which explains why the cost of debt is lowered by $(1 - t)$.

What determines the value of λ? Lenders want to see strong sponsor commitment to the project, which means considerable equity commitment. There should also be adequate debt service cover, that is, net earnings must cover periodic debt repayment. Combining these two considerations, λ ranges from 0.6 to 0.9 for infrastructure projects, with a mean of about 0.7.

The cost of a bank loan (r_d) is the best rate quoted by competing syndicates for the project loan package. If the SPV issues a bond during the operation phase, the cost of the bond depends on the coupon payment. For example, the cost of a \$1,000 bond that pays \$50 a year is 5%. It needs to be adjusted for issuance cost and corporate tax.

The cost of equity may be estimated using Gordon's formula. Suppose a company's stock with similar risks to the SPV earns a dividend D_1 at the end of the first year, and this dividend grows at the rate of g% per year. The current value (V) of the share is the present value of future dividends, that is,

$$V = D_1/(1 + r_e) + D_1(1 + g)/(1 + r_e)^2 + \cdots = D_1/(r_e - g).$$

Hence,

$$r_e = g + D_1/V.$$

For example, if the company's share currently trading at \$1.20 provides a dividend of 6c very year, its cost of equity is $r_e = 0 + 6/120 = 0.05$ or 5%.

An alternative approach is to use the Capital Asset Pricing Model or CAPM, that is,

$$r_e = r_f + \beta(r_m - r_f).$$

Here r_e is the expected cost of equity, r_f is the risk-free interest rate, β is the beta for the company, and r_m is the expected market rate of return. Some texts use $E[r_e]$ and $E[r_m]$ to make it explicit that they refer to expectations. The expected value of a variable X, written as $E[X]$, is the population mean. The expected market return can be approximated using the market index (e.g. 5%). The risk-free rate is approximated by the rate on long-term government bonds (e.g. 2.5%). The term $(r_m - r_f)$ represents the market risk premium. Hence $\beta(r_m - r_f)$ represents the risk premium for the company's share. If $\beta = 1$, the company's share is as risky as that of the market. If $\beta < 1$, the company's share is less risky, that is, it is a defensive stock. If $\beta > 1$, the company's share is riskier than that of the market index. For example, if $\beta = 1.2$, then

$$r_e = r_f + \beta(r_m - r_f) = 2.5\% + 1.2(5\% - 2.5\%) = 5.5\%.$$

To find the value of β for a company, we can use regression by rewriting the CAPM model as

$$(r_e - r_f) = \alpha + \beta(r_m - r_f) + \varepsilon.$$

This is the same as the simple regression model

$$y = \alpha + \beta x + \varepsilon.$$

Here α is the intercept and ε is the error term. We can use about five years of monthly data for the regression. In practice, stockbrokers routinely publish and update the betas of most companies to save you the effort.

Loan repayments

For a $\$L$ loan (the principal) at annual interest rate i, the *annual* constant repayment amount to amortize or fully repay the loan in n years is

$$Z = Li/H \quad \text{where} \quad H = 1 - (1 + i)^{-n}.$$

Here n is called the amortization period. The *monthly* repayment is

$$Z_m = L(i/12)/G \quad \text{where} \quad G = 1 - [1 + (i/12)]^{-12n}.$$

Observe that $Z \neq 12Z_m$ or $Z/Z_m \neq 12$. That is, 12 monthly repayments do not equal one annual repayment. The correct relation is

$$Z/Z_m = [Li/H]/[L(i/12)/G] = 12G/H.$$

Table 7.1   Amortizing loan repayment table.

Year	Principal at start of period	Annual repayment	Payment of	
			Interest	Principal
1	1,000	367	50	317
2	683	367	34	333
3	350	367	17	350
4	0			

Example: Amortizing loan repayment table

Consider a loan with $L = \$1,000$, annual interest rate $(i) = 0.05$, and $n = 3$ years. The annual repayment to amortize the loan is

$$Z = 1,000(0.05)/H = \$367, \qquad \text{where } H = 1 - (1 + 0.05)^{-3}.$$

We use the following steps to construct Table 7.1:

- If $n = 3$, construct 4 rows so that for Year 4, the principal at start of period should be 0 to amortize the loan.
- Fill in the principal amount ($1,000) and annual repayment ($367) for Year 1.
- For Year 1, Interest payment = Principal at start of period ($1,000) × Interest rate (0.05) = $50. Payment of principal = 367 − 50 = $317.
- For Year 2, Principal at start of period = 1,000 − 317 = $683. Interest payment = 0.05(683) = $34. Payment of principal = 367 − 34 = $333.
- For Year 3, Principal at start of period is 683 − 333 = $350. Interest payment = 0.05(350) = $17. Payment of principal = 367 − 17 = $350.
- For Year 4, Principal at start of period = 350 − 350 = $0.

Not all loans are amortizing, such as the following repayment schemes for a $70 loan in a week:

1	2	3	4	5	6	7
$10	$10	$10	$10	$10	$10	$10
$1	$1	$1	$1	$1	$1	$64

Assume that there is no interest on the loan to simplify the discussion. In the first scheme, equal repayments of $10 each day reduces the debt to zero by the end of the week. In the second scheme, equal repayments of $1 each day reduces the debt to $64 at the end of the week. This *balloon loan* is useful if the borrower does not have adequate funds to repay $10 a day. For example, in a 7-year housing loan, the rent may not cover the periodic loan repayment. The investor or borrower may request for a balloon loan to reduce his annual cash outlay. At the end of the 7th year, he will sell the house and use the proceeds to repay the remaining debt.

We can apply the same principle to an infrastructure project that generates low cash flows during the initial periods. If these cash flows are insufficient to cover periodic debt repayment, a balloon loan may be suitable.

Example: Balloon loan repayment table

Consider a $1,000 loan ($L$) with annual interest rate (i) of 5 percent, a term (T) of 3 years, and an amortization period (n) of 10 years. The difference between T and n is that the loan must be fully repaid by T, and n is the number of periods used to compute the periodic repayment. If $n = T$, the debt will be zero at the end of the term, as in the previous example. If $n > T$, it is a balloon loan (Table 7.2).

The annual repayment is

$$Z = 1,000(0.05)/H = \$130, \quad \text{where } H = 1 - (1 + 0.05)^{-10}.$$

At the end of the 3-year term, the borrower must pay the remaining $748.

Table 7.2   Loan repayment table for a balloon loan.

Year	Principal at start of period	Annual repayment	Payment of interest	Principal
1	1,000	130	50	80
2	920	130	46	84
3	836	130	42	88
4	748			

Currency risks

Currency risks include sales, purchases, and loan repayments in different currencies as well as restrictions on foreign currency transactions. If the project is in a developing country, sponsors may not be able to secure sufficient local currency loans to match its revenues because the financial market is not well developed. This financing gap exposes the SPV (borrower) to currency fluctuations that are difficult to predict.

Sponsors may mitigate the impact by indexing output price (i.e. project revenues) to the exchange rate. Clearly, this requires the agreement of the purchaser in the off-take contract.

An alternative strategy is a *currency swap*. Suppose a project borrows at 6% in a foreign currency (FC) such as the US dollar but revenues are in the local currency (LC). It can arrange with a swap bank to pay 6% in FC and receive 8% in LC. Its net position is as follows:

Pay lender	6% in FC
Receive from swap bank	6% in FC
Pay swap bank	8% in LC
Net position	8% in LC

Effectively, the SPV is paying 8% in LC, which matches its revenues. It receives 6% in FC from the swap bank to pay its lender.

To overcome restrictions on foreign currency transactions, sponsors may set up an offshore escrow account. An offshore banking account is a bank account with a financial institution outside the home country. An escrow is a financial arrangement where the third party (e.g. a bank) holds and regulates payment of funds between two parties (e.g. SPV and off-taker). The purchaser or off-taker will pay in hard currency to this account.

Alternatively, the SPV may try to obtain a government guarantee on foreign currency availability.

Example: Fluctuations in Renminbi

Predicting currency movements is not easy. In this example, we consider fluctuations in the Chinese Yuan, or Renminbi (RMB). The textbook theory is that a country with continuing large trade surplus will see an appreciation of the currency because of greater demand for the currency. In turn, the appreciation will cheapen imports and make exports more expensive, which will reduce the trade surplus.

The puzzle is the slow movement of the RMB despite the large annual trade surplus (US$422 billion in 2019). China's trade competitors tend to see it as reflecting a deliberate attempt by a "currency manipulator" to undervalue the RMB to boost exports. In early 2014, the exchange rate was about 6 RMB to the US dollar. The rate in July 2020 was about 7 RMB. The RMB has weakened rather than strengthened against the US dollar over this period despite the rising trade surplus.

In the mid-1990s, the RMB was tied to the US dollar to suppress inflation and avoid foreign exchange instability. With the growing strength of the Chinese economy, the tie is no longer necessary. Chinese authorities then use the surplus dollars from trade to invest in US government bonds and other assets. As of April 2020, they hold US$1.073 trillion of bonds excluding Hong Kong's US$243 billion.

A Chinese exporter who is paid in US dollars will need to exchange it for RMB with a Chinese bank to pay his workers, rent, utilities, taxes, and inputs. The Chinese bank then exchanges its dollar holdings for RMB with the Chinese Central Bank. The Central Bank issues bonds to soak up the excess amounts of RMB swirling in the economy, which explains the relatively low inflation despite the huge trade surplus. Observe that, at the end of the process, the Central Bank has the dollars.

Inflation risk

The causes of inflation are demand and supply of goods and services. On the demand side, excessive purchasing power, such as by increasing money supply, will result in a rise in the general of prices. On the supply or cost side, prices may increase because of rising wages and supply restrictions or disruptions. These disruptions may be caused by labor strikes, natural disasters, war, and so on.

A price rise in one sector may not lead to a general rise in prices because buyers will seek cheaper substitutes. However, some commodities such as oil are used in many sectors and have few substitutes. Hence, there is a tendency to associate rising oil prices with inflation.

To mitigation inflation risk in a project, it is common to index prices to inflation. In energy-intensive projects, there is often a pass-through arrangement linking output prices to fluctuations in input energy prices.

Interest rate risk

Like all commodities, the level of interest rates depends on the demand and supply for loanable funds. The demand for funds depends on expected profitability and cost of funds. The supply of funds depends on money supply, interest rates, and how banks feel about business conditions.

Globally, real interest rates tend to follow the US rate because mobile funds or "hot money" flow to high-interest financial assets. These flows affect the currency exchange rates. If speculators and investors sense that a country may devalue its currency because of balance of pay-ments difficulties, there will be capital flight. Investors will sell financial and real assets in the local currency and convert the funds into hard currencies.

One way to mitigate interest rate risk is to negotiate for a fixed rate loan that will be higher than a floating rate loan to compensate the lender for the risk. Another possibility is to arrange for collared financing where interest rates fall within a range, say 5 to 10 percent. The borrower pays no more than the upper limit. However, if interest rates fall below the lower limit, the lender will charge the lower limit. It may also be possible to negotiate for the flexibility to convert from floating to fixed rates.

Sponsors can also arrange for an *interest rate swap* with a swap bank. Suppose the SPV borrows at S + 2% where S is the Singapore Interbank Offered Rate (SIBOR) or the Singapore Overnight Rate Average (SORA) based on overnight domestic cash transactions. It may arrange to swap it with another bank by paying 3% fixed and receiving S%. The net position of the SPV is as follows:

Pay to lender	S + 2%
Pay to swap bank	3% fixed
Receive from swap bank	S%
Total payment	S + 5%
Total receipt	S%
Net position	5% fixed

Swaptions are options on interest rate swaps. For example, a call swaption gives the holder the right but not the obligation to enter into an interest rate swap.

Financial feasibility

We are now ready to put together the above elements and determine the financial feasibility of a project. There are three main tables, namely,

- the income statement;
- the cash flow table; and
- the balance sheet.

Usually, we perform financial ratio analyses based on the above tables to check the SPV's liquidity, efficiency, profitability, and solvency.

Income statement

The income statement is also known as the profit and loss statement. It shows the profit or loss for a particular year or over several years (Table 7.3). As the PPP contract has not yet been awarded, the figures in the sponsor's income statement are projected values. The figures in the table are merely for illustration.

For project assessments over several years, it is better to use real rather than nominal values to simplify the analysis.

The cost of goods sold are factory or site costs. They include production cost of materials, labor, factory overhead, and transport. If desired, these costs can be reflected as line items.

Table 7.3   Income statement ($m).

	Year 1	Year 2, etc.
Revenue	30	
Less: Cost of goods sold	15	
Selling, general and administrative expenses	5	
Operating profit (EBITDA)	**10**	
Less: Depreciation	5	
Interest expense	1	
Corporate tax	1	
Net profit	**3**	

The selling, general, and administrative expenses (SGA) are head office costs. They include marketing, sales, management, insurance, legal expenses, secretariat, office supplies, utilities, and office equipment.

EBITDA stands for earnings before interest, tax, depreciation, and amortization. Investment is booked as annual depreciation rather than as an initial lump sum to better reflect profit from operation. The depreciation amount depends on tax laws. If straight-line depreciation is used, the annual depreciation of an asset is

$$A = (I - S)/T.$$

Here I is the initial investment, S is the salvage value, and T is the allowable depreciation period. For example, if an asset costs $10 m with a salvage value of $2 m and the allowable period is 8 years, then

$$A = (10 - 2)/8 = \$1 \text{ m.}$$

The SPV will have different assets, and needs to work out the depreciation allowances separately, excluding land which cannot be depreciated because it is assumed to be indestructible. The term "amortization" in EBITDA refers to depreciation of intangible assets such as trademarks, patents, copyright, and goodwill. It should not be confused with the amortization of a loan discussed earlier in this chapter under "sources and cost of funds."

After deducting depreciation, interest expense, and corporate tax, we obtain the net profit. Interest is an expense if the company is paying off a loan.

Some items that are not reflected in Table 7.3, and should be reported separately. For example, if the company puts its cash as deposits, it earns interest income. Thus, interest is not necessarily an expense. Further, there may be extraordinary charges or credits such as losses due to disasters, gain or loss from a law suit, or a windfall gain by winning a lottery. These gains or losses can be large, and may distort the income statement. These items should be reported separately.

Cash flow statement

The cash flow statement shows cash inflows and outflows over the period of the project, that is, from Year 0 to n (Table 7.4). As before, it is better to use real values to simplify the handling of inflation.

Table 7.4   Cash flow statement ($m).

	0	1	...	n
Cash flow from operations				
Net profit	3			
Depreciation	5			
Change in working capital	0			
Cash flow from investing activities				
Sale/purchase of property, plant and equipment	−10			
Sale/purchase of long-term financial assets	0			
Sale/purchase of patents, trademarks, licenses	0			
Cash flow from financing activities				
Proceeds from bank loans	10			
Repayment of funds borrowed	0			
Sale/purchase of marketable securities	0			
Equity issued	2			
Dividends paid out	−1			
Net cash flow	**9**	**10**		
Cash balance at beginning of period	0	9		
Cash balance at end of period	9	19		

The cash flow from operations are taken from the previous Income Statement. The new item is change in working capital to reflect changes in accounts receivable, inventories, and accounts payable. For example, an increase in inventory uses cash, and is booked as a negative value.

For investing activities, every sale of assets produces cash, and every purchase reduces cash. In this example, the firm spent $10 m to purchase property, plant or equipment.

For financing activities, the firm received $10 m as a loan, issued $2 m of equity, and paid out $1 m in dividends.

The net cash flow is the sum of cash flows from operations, investing activities, and financing activities. Finally, we may compute the cumulative cash balance for each year.

Equity internal rate of return

Sponsors are interested in the return on their investment, which is equity. Hence, they are interested in cash flows. Suppose a project incurs an initial equity of $30 m and positive cash flows thereafter:

Year 0	Year 1	Year 2	Year 3	Year 4
−$30 m	$10 m	$10 m	$10 m	$10 m

The equity internal rate of return (IRR), q, for the project is found by solving

$$0 = -30 + 10/(1 + q) + \cdots + 10/(1 + q)^4.$$

Using trial and error, $q = 12.6\%$. It is worth repeating that the figures in the table are cash flows, not project benefits and costs.

Balance sheet

The Balance Sheet shows a firm's financial health at a particular date such as 31 December 20xx (Table 7.5). It uses accrual accounting, that is,

- revenue is recognized in the period in which the good is sold or service is performed irrespective of whether the firm is paid; and
- the accrual principle also applies to the expense side to match expenses to revenues.

Table 7.5 Balance sheet.

Assets ($m)		Liabilities ($m)	
Current assets		**Current liabilities**	
Cash and marketable securities	20	Accounts payable	14
Accounts receivable	50	Dividend and taxes payable	6
Inventories	40	Short-term loans	10
Total current assets	110	Total current liabilities	30
Long-term assets		**Long-term liabilities**	
Land and buildings	50	Bank loans	20
Machinery and equipment	30	Bonds	30
Less accumulated depreciation	(10)		
Intangible assets	10		
Less accumulated amortization	(5)		
Total assets	185	**Total liabilities**	80
		Net worth (shareholders' equity)	105

The current assets and liabilities refer to short-term items of less than a year such as cash and marketable securities, accounts receivable, and inventories of goods and materials. Long-term assets include buildings, machinery, and equipment. These assets need to be depreciated except for land. Depreciation for intangible assets such as patents and trademarks is called amortization.

On the liability side, the firm has short-term liabilities that it needs to pay out within a year, such as accounts payable, dividends and taxes payable, and short-term loans. It also has long-term liabilities such as bank loans and bonds. The difference between assets and liabilities is the firm's net worth or shareholders' equity. It comprises common stock paid in by shareholders and retained profits. The Balance Sheet must balance, that is, Total assets = Total liabilities + Net worth.

Table 7.6   Examples of financial ratios.

Ratio	
Liquidity	Current ratio = Current assets/Current liabilities
	Cash ratio = (Cash and marketable securities)/Current liabilities
Efficiency	Inventory turnover = Cost of goods sold*/Average inventory
	Asset turnover ratio = Revenue*/Total assets
Profitability	Gross profit margin = Gross profit*/Revenue*
	Return on assets = Net profit*/Total assets
Solvency	Debt to equity ratio = Total liability/Total debt
	Interest coverage ratio = Operating profit*/Interest expenses*

Ratio analysis

Lenders and investors routinely use ratio analysis to assess the performance of a firm. The key ratios are

- liquidity ratios;
- efficiency ratios;
- profitability ratios; and
- solvency ratios.

Most of the figures for the ratios are taken from the Income Statement or Balance Sheet. In Table 7.6, variables with an asterisk are taken from the Income Statement; the rest are from the Balance Sheet. Within each category, there are many ratios and Table 7.6 provides two examples of each.

Normally, we compare these ratios with those from similar firms in the industry or with rules of thumb. We also track changes in these ratios over time. Any substantial deviation warrants some explanation; for example, a firm may have a much higher debt to equity ratio, signaling excessive borrowing.

Project insurances

As part of project preparations, sponsors have to consider insurance. The basis of insurance is often claims-made, that is, claims must be made before expiry of policy. There is also excess, an amount below which the policy holder has to foot the bill. For example, if there is an excess of $1,000 on a car insurance, the insurer will not pay for any damage below this amount. There are also monetary cover limits beyond which a policy holder cannot claim.

Political risk insurance provides cover against political events that lead to loss, such as terrorism, expropriation, civil unrest, and so on (see Table 3.3). Such insurances may be purchased from multilateral development banks or private insurers.

Work injury compensation insurance is usually a statutory requirement for all employees or those earning below a certain salary. It covers injury or death on no-blame basis, that is, an injured worker will be compensated even if he is at fault. However, if a worker feels that the payout is not sufficient, he may forgo it and sue the employer instead. Employers may want to insure against this possibility by purchasing *employer's liability insurance*. In addition, the contractor needs to insure his property, vehicles, machinery, and other assets.

It is common for the contractor to purchase *builder's risk insurance* and include the premium as part of the bid. In some projects, the sponsor (owner) purchases the insurance but she may not be familiar. Hence, it is more common for the contractor to purchase it. The sum insured is the normally the estimated project value and covers project works, temporary structures, and materials (on site, in transit or stored off-site) against named perils such as water and fire damage, theft, and mistakes. Normally, it excludes major catastrophes, damage to project documents, reworks, and faulty design. In some cases, it may be possible for the local insurer to re-insure catastrophic risks with an international insurer who can diversify the risks across many cities on a global scale. Sponsors have to conduct their due diligence to ensure that the contractor obtains adequate insurance without too many qualifications.

A *general liability insurance* (GL insurance) protects the insured against third-party claims for property damage or injury. For example, a crane may damage an adjoining property or a pedestrian is hit by falling debris. The contractor either purchases GL insurance separately or include it as part of builder's risk insurance, which then becomes a *builder's all-risk insurance*. The term is misleading because there are exclusions, as discussed above. Normally, the sponsor is included as an *additional insured* party because the neighbor whose property is damaged may sue the sponsor and contractor. The sponsor, as an additional insured party, may file a claim to cover her loss.

It is possible to include *environmental liability insurance* to cover clean-up cost under the builder's risk insurance. If it is not possible, the contractor has to purchase separate insurance under similar arrangements.

Sponsors need to ensure that consultants have professional indemnity insurance, also called *professional liability insurance*. It covers consultants' inadequate advice, services, or designs due to errors and omissions (mistakes) or negligence (carelessness) that cause the SPV to lose money. If the SPV sues the consultant, the insurance should cover the legal costs of the consultant and any award to the sponsor.

If the project is delayed, the SPV may suffer from *consequential loss* of revenue. It is possible to purchase insurance for start-up delay or rely on liquidated damages from the contractor to cover the loss.

Finally, sponsors need to purchase *operation and maintenance insurances*. These insurances include

- operator's all risk insurance to cover property damage, injury, and general liability to third parties;
- machinery breakdown; and
- business disruption.

Since the SPV has a project loan, the lender will require that the benefits of insurance be assigned through *lender's clauses* in the policy. If the SPV defaults on the loan, the lender has the right to the benefits.

Over the years, insurers have developed new instruments to insure against different types of project risks. An example is a catastrophe bond, as explained in the following example.

Example: Catastrophe bond

If a project such as a hydropower plant is to be located in an earthquake zone, it may not be able to find a local insurer with the capacity to insure against an earthquake. Sometimes, the local insurer may take the risk and reinsures with an international insurer. The latter is better able to spread the risks globally; after all, earthquakes do not happen all at once in different places around the world.

Another possible solution is for the insurer to issue catastrophe bonds, or cat bonds, to investors. The insurer sets up a special purpose entity (not to be confused with the project SPV) to

- receive premiums from policy holders (e.g. the infrastructure project company);
- issue cat bonds to investors; and
- invest the premiums and investors' funds for stable returns.

The cat bond is generally of short duration, such as three years. If the earthquake does not happen, investors get back their principal in addition to periodic coupons. Cat bond coupons pay higher interest to compensate investors for the higher risk.

If an earthquake occurs as defined by pre-determined triggers (e.g. above a certain value on the Richter scale), investors will get back part of the principal depending on the extent of damage. The insurer will recall the invested funds and use them to pay policy holders for the earthquake damage. The remaining unused funds will be returned to cat bond holders. To incentivize investors, the insurer is likely to limit the insurance payouts and protect part of the principal.

Draft shareholders' agreements

At the end of the bid preparation stage, sponsors take into consideration all the issues and draft the shareholders' arrangements and project agreements (Table 7.7). Subsequently, lenders will draft the loan and security documents, Shareholders' Support Agreement, and Direct Agreement (see Chapter 8). They will also provide inputs or require changes to other agreements to protect the lenders' interest. The grantor will draft the PPP contract or the off-take contract (see Chapter 5). If the buyer of the project output is a private entity, the SPV will draft the off-take contract.

We have dealt with the *Development Agreement* at the start of this chapter. The *Shareholders' Agreement* covers

Table 7.7   Project contracts and agreements.

Shareholders' agreements
Development Agreement
Shareholders' Agreement
Shareholders' Support Agreement
Loan and security documents
Loan Agreement
Security Agreement
Equity Support Agreement
Common Terms Agreement
Accounts Agreement
Inter-creditor Agreement
Project agreements
PPP Contract
Direct Agreement
Construction Contract
Operation and Maintenance Contract
Offtake Agreement
Fuel Supply Agreement
Land Lease Agreement
Equipment Contract

- the establishment of SPV;
- shareholding, funding, and management;
- additional equity for cost overrun;
- bank guarantee on obligations;
- dividend policy, in-kind contribution, and disposal of shares;
- conflict of interest such as if the contractor or operator is also a shareholder;
- undertakings not to engage in activities in competition with the SPV; and
- dispute resolution.

Lenders may require a *Shareholders' Support Agreement* that covers

- technical support;
- further equity contributions;
- restrictions on disposal of shares; and
- completion, cost overrun, and liquidated damages guarantees.

Draft project agreements

Direct agreement

The grantor, lender, and SPV sign a Direct Agreement to allow the lender to *step in* if the SPV defaults on its loan. This tri-partite arrangement will require negotiations among the parties. The lender will try to "cure" the project if the default is temporary. The cure period may last up to three years. If the project is in serious trouble, lenders may replace the management team and novate the project agreements. The lender will also step in to secure project assets and agreements over third-party claims, such as that of contractor, subcontractors, and suppliers.

The grantor may step in if the project suffers from serious performance lapses, threatens national security, or raises serious environmental concerns or public health. For example, it may step in, in the public interest, if a water desalination project does not deliver sufficient quantities of water. The grantor may compensate the SPV for the present value of the asset and take over its operations.

In some countries, there are no step-in rights for lenders or grantors. In countries with step-in rights, lenders have reservations on the ability of the grantor to step in because of possible loss on the loan. There is also the question of who to step in first if the SPV defaults on the loan as well as on its obligations to the grantor.

Construction contract

The clauses in the Construction Contract will depend on the type of project delivery (see Table 3.1). Lenders prefer traditional fixed price contracts for building projects to mitigate risks of price escalation. For process projects, the EPC contract is preferred to provide a single point of responsibility. The standard conditions of contract for building works are given below as an example:

- Definitions, interpretations, and applicable laws;
- Consultants' representatives;
- Contract documents;
- General obligations of contractor;
- Sub-surface and ground conditions;
- Contractor's design responsibility;
- Acceleration of works;
- Liquidated damages;
- Substantial completion;
- Quality standards and defects;
- Variation of works;
- Notices and fees;
- Site surveys;
- Project program;
- Extension of time;
- Site possession and commencement of works;
- Suspension of works;
- Measurement of works;
- Claims;
- Construction plant and equipment;
- Temporary works, materials, and goods;
- Indemnity provisions;
- Insurances;
- Subcontractors;
- Termination;
- Progress payment;
- Final account;
- Fluctuations;
- Final completion; and
- Dispute resolution.

In some projects, there may be special conditions such as incentive payments for early completion, advance payment for materials or mobilization, assignment of rights to lenders, early occupation of site, and so on. These conditions are consolidated under a separate document called "Special conditions of contract."

There are many standard forms of contracts drafted by civil engineers, government agencies, developers, architects, and international bodies (Haswell and de Silva, 1989; Ramus *et al.*, 2006; Lim, 2020). These forms may represent particular interests and need to be used with care.

Operation and maintenance contract

The Operation and Maintenance (O&M) Contract may contain the following provisions:

- contract period;
- scope of services comprising
  - o operations, including training of operatives;
  - o maintenance, that is, routine maintenance, corrective maintenance (repairs), preventive maintenance (regular inspection and servicing), and cyclical works; and
  - o other services such as participation in commissioning tests, security, emergency, waste management, energy conservation, renovations, and leasing.
- performance-based fees;
- performance standards;
- limits on operator's authority regarding disposal of assets, contracting, and reimbursable expenses not in conformity with budget;
- operator's assistance in obtaining statutory permits and approvals;
- guarantee of compliance with the law;
- operator's insurances;
- indemnity;
- monthly and annual progress reports;
- SPV's right to inspect facilities and operations;
- SPV's right to inspect and audit records;
- early termination; and
- dispute resolution.

The O&M Contract will also normally stipulate the owner's responsibility to

- provide manuals, list of spares, and drawings;
- provide feedstock, site access, and utilities;
- approve budget and operating plans;
- pay reimbursable costs;
- engage external parties for major works beyond the scope of services provided by the operator; and
- develop a standard operating procedures (SOP) manual on reporting, accounting, contracting, and record-keeping.

Off-take agreement

The Off-take Agreement covers

- type of purchase contract, preferably "take or pay" where the buyer has to pay for a minimum amount of the output even if he does not take delivery;
- payment mechanism;
- adjustment for inflation and currency movements, if any;
- pass-through provisions, if any;
- penalties for poor performance;
- inter-connection facilities;
- transport and storage requirements;
- termination;
- force majeure provisions; and
- dispute resolution.

Supply agreement

There are many types of supply and purchase agreements depending on the role of the SPV in the supply chain. For example, if the SPV owns the pipeline that transports natural gas, it signs a *Through-put Agreement* to transport the gas at a specific price on a monthly basis. In contrast, if the SPV processes the raw materials, it signs a *Tolling Agreement* to charge the counter-party for the processing.

A *Fuel Supply Agreement* is often a "supply or pay" contract with a credit-worthy and reliable supplier. The credit worthiness is required in case the supplier needs to pay liquidated damages. The agreement will stipulate the supply price, range of quantities, and interconnection facilities provided by the supplier. Both sides will need to back their commitments, such as with Letters of Credit.

Other agreements

A *Land Lease Agreement* stipulates the appropriate land use, term of lease, rent, payable tax, renewal options, responsibilities for repairs and maintenance, and condition of land at the end of the lease. The owner, usually the government in PPP projects, will want to retain the right of access.

An *Equipment Contract* for major equipment often contain the following provisions:

- specifications;
- price, taxes, and import duties;
- milestone dates;
- delivery arrangements including insurance, transport, and handling charges;
- installation, inspection, commissioning tests, certification, completion, and taking over of ownership;
- possible defects, acceptance, payment, retention, and liquidated damages;
- warranty;
- maintenance and repair contract (if any), including schedule of rates;
- training of operatives;
- manuals and list of spares; and
- dispute resolution.

Business case

The last step in the bid preparation is to write the business case to seek parent company approval and secure project financing. The business will cover most of the items discussed in this chapter, such as

- project information;
- shareholding structure;
- project governance structure;
- design proposal;
- price proposal;
- political, regulatory, and legal assessments;
- projected revenue;
- cost and schedule estimates;
- quality measures;
- inputs;
- operation and maintenance;
- force majeure risks;
- hedging instruments;
- project insurances;
- draft shareholders' agreements;
- draft project agreements; and
- financing strategy.

The financing strategy will include proposed equity contributions and the amount of loan requested.

The information is confidential, and sponsors will have to decide what to include and exclude when presenting the business case to lenders.

References

Haswell, C. and de Silva, D. (1989) *Civil engineering contracts*. London: Butterworth.

Joshi, M. (2010) *The concepts and practice of mathematical finance*. London: Cambridge University Press.

KPMG (2010) *PPP procurement: Review of barriers to competition and efficiency in the procurement of PPP projects*. Sydney: KPMG.

Lim, P. (2020) *Contract administration and procurement in the Singapore construction industry*. S'pore: World Scientific.

McDonald, R. (2014) *Derivatives markets*. Harlow: Pearson.

Ramus, J., Birchall, S., and Griffiths, P. (2006) *Contract practice for surveyors — Fourth Edition*. London: Butterworth-Heinemann.

Tan, W. (2018) *Research methods: A practical guide for students and researchers*. Singapore: World Scientific.

CHAPTER 8

Bid evaluation and contract award

Price bidding strategies

As discussed in the previous chapter, the grantor evaluates bids for infrastructure projects on design, price, and other criteria on a weighted basis. The weights, which tend to be ad-hoc, depend on the grantor's priority. In this section, we consider only price bids or auctions using the highest or lowest price.

If the grantor is the buyer (off-taker) of the project output, such as in desalination projects, the bid is based on the lowest price. If the grantor is the seller, such as in 5G mobile spectrum auctions, it is based on the highest price. To simplify the discussion, we will consider bidding based on the highest price as the principles are easily extended to bids based on the lowest price. Further, in line with auction theory, we will use the terms "auction" and "tender" interchangeably.

There are many types of auctions (Klemperer, 2014; Krishna, 2009). Let H be the highest bidder, and S be the second highest bidder. The *English auction* uses *open* bidding. It starts with a floor or reserved price and bids are progressively raised until there is only one bid left, the highest bid. H pays slightly above the second highest valuation. If the highest valuation is $100 and the second highest is $90, bidding stops at $91. The *Japanese auction* is similar except that the price increase is automatic in small increments and time intervals until only a single buyer remains in the auction room.

In a *Dutch auction*, open bidding starts with a high price set by the seller and this is progressively lowered until someone raises her hand. This bidding process is often faster than the English auction because it takes only one bid to decide the outcome. Again, the winning bid is near the second highest valuation. Using the same example, H will not raise her hand at $100 because it yields no profit. If she expects a 10% profit, then bidding should stop around $90.

The *Vickrey* (1961) *auction* uses *sealed* bids and the winning bidder pays the second highest bid and not what she bids. The optimal strategy is to bid at valuation because if you win, you pay the second highest bid. Hence *H* will bid $100, *S* will bid $90, and *H* pays $90.

Finally, consider a *sealed bid auction* where you pay what you bid and not the second highest bid. Again, *H* will not bid $100 because it yields no profit. Hence, she will bid around $90, that is, what she thinks is the second highest bid.

In summary, the English, Japanese, Dutch, Vickrey, and sealed bid auctions give the same result, that is, the winner pays the second highest valuation. But is it worth it? We have to consider the winner's curse.

Winner's curse

The winner's curse is the difference between a winning bid and the true worth of an item. The difference between the winning and second bid is not a winner's curse but probably a winner's regret.

Over-bidding can arise if a bidder is emotional or desperate, or if the bidding environment is intense and competitive. It can also occur for strategic reasons, such as to gain experience, enter a market, or deter competitors from entering the market. A winner's curse need not always exist. A bidder may have private information about the value of the item that is not available to other bidders, as distinct from common value auctions where bidders do not have such private information. This brings us to how imperfect and asymmetric information may lead to over-bidding.

Imperfect and asymmetric information

For infrastructure projects, a major cause of over-bidding is information imperfection or asymmetry. Information is imperfect if it is not fully known. It is asymmetric if one party has better information than the other. The revenues, costs, and risks are only estimates and not fully known. Hence, there is the possibility of forecasting errors (Standard and Poor's, 2002). Thus, one way to minimize or avoid the winner's curse is to do your homework and use appropriate valuation techniques (Ferris and Petitt, 2002). Another approach is to bid more conservatively. Finally, the winner's curse may also be smaller if there is opportunity to renegotiate the PPP contract early in the concession period (Guasch, 2004).

Apart from the winner's curse, asymmetric information causes problems relating to quality, effort, action, and the future. The issues and mitigation strategies are given in Table 3.4, and should be incorporated into contracts.

Bid evaluation

The evaluation of bids depends on whether bid arrangement uses one or two stages (Asian Development Bank, 2018). Where possible, the opening of bids is public in the interest of transparency.

Recall that a Public Private Partnership (PPP) contract is awarded to the lowest or highest bidder depending on whether the grantor is the buyer or seller respectively. For the rest of this section, we will assume that the lowest bid wins the contract to avoid repetition. An evaluation team carries out the evaluation, which may take weeks, or even months. At the end of the tender, the team prepares a tender evaluation report.

For one-stage bids, the grantor awards the contract based on

- price alone;
- design (technical) and price; or
- best value, that is, design, price, and other criteria.

The grantor will reject bids with deficient designs, that is, those with critical deviations from specifications. The other criteria include financial strength, innovation, track record, environmental sustainability, operation and maintenance regime, and schedule. Usually, a simple points system is used.

In complex projects, the grantor may use a two-stage bid process. In the first stage, bidders submit design or technical proposals only. The grantor evaluates the technical proposals and allows bidders to make adjustments or drop out of the competition. In the second stage, bidders submit approved technical and price proposals. The grantor then uses a points system to evaluate the tender.

There are a number of issues in evaluating bids. The first issue is price adjustments for minor technical deviations. The practice varies, but it is common to allow for minor price variations.

Second, there are issues with

- having one bidder only;
- no conforming bids; and
- abnormally low bids.

The grantor is not obliged to award the contract if the responses are not favorable. If there is only one bidder, it is possible to award the contract after conducting internal due diligence or repackage it and re-tender. An abnormally low bid may signal misreading or misunderstanding of the project requirements, mismeasurement, desperation for work, or the efficiency of the bidder. It is rare for an efficient bidder to submit very low bids.

Third, there is the issue of admissibility of alternative designs or bids with qualifications that include or exclude certain items. Bidders may suggest changes to improve the design, and the grantor should welcome such suggestions. Normally, the tender conditions stipulate the admissibility of such suggestions but the grantor will award the contract based on the original design.

Award of contract

The grantor will inform the winning bidder, usually within a few months. She will also inform unsuccessful bidders.

The next step is to negotiate with the bidder on implementation arrangements such as the nomination of coordinators for each party and timelines to finalize third-party contracts and agreements as well as reach financial close. Depending on the complexity of the project and the financial environment, it may take up to a year to reach financial close. Thereafter, both parties will sign the PPP contract. If the site is not ready, the grantor will provide a Letter of Intent. Otherwise, the contract clock starts when the grantor provides the winning bidder with a Notice to Proceed.

References

Asian Development Bank (2018) *Guide on bid evaluation.* Manila: ADB.

Ferris, K. and Pettit, B. (2002) *Valuation: Avoiding the winner's curse.* New Jersey: Prentice Hall.

Guasch, J. (2004) *Granting and renegotiating infrastructure concessions: Doing it right.* Washington: World Bank Institute.

Klemperer, P. (2014) *Auctions: Theory and practice.* New Jersey: Princeton University Press.

Krishna, V. (2009) *Auction theory.* New York: Academic Press.

Standard and Poor's (2002) *Traffic forecasting risk in start-up toll facilities.* London: Standard and Poor.

Vickrey, W. (1961) Counter-speculation, auctions, and competitive sealed tenders. *Journal of Finance*, 16(1), 8–37.

CHAPTER 9

Lender's due diligence

In-principle approval

Once the sponsors decide to bid for a project, the financing process gets underway. They will explore the market to determine the best financing package among groups of syndicated lenders. Sponsors may approach certain lenders where they have previous business dealings or issue a Request for Proposal (RFP) for lenders to bid.

Lenders conduct due diligence before issuing in-principle approval to fund the project if the borrower (sponsor) wins the Public Private Partnership (PPP) contract. The due diligence is required because of information imperfection and asymmetry, that is, profitability is based on forecast revenues and costs, and borrowers may hide or under-estimate the real project risks to secure funding at lower cost or better terms. Raising the interest rate may not deter risky borrowers; if anything, it increases the risk of default. Other than due diligence, lenders reduce their risk exposure by forming syndicates and by lowering the quantum of the loan. Collectively, these tactics are called non-price measures (Harris, 1974).

After the PPP contract award, depending on the size and nature of the project, sponsors have about three to six months to reach financial close. In some cases, the period may be extended, such as during a financial crisis when credit is tight. The lead arranger of the syndicate may underwrite the entire loan, that is, it will absorb the difference if the syndicate is unable to raise the loan amount. Alternatively, it may underwrite only a part of the loan, called a "best-efforts" deal. Finally, in a "club deal," the lead arranger does not underwrite the loan. Instead, a club or group of banks issue the loans together.

Borrower's background

Lenders begin their due diligence by studying the borrower's background, business model, track record, financials, and resources. The borrower must have a sound business strategy, and the project's goals and objectives are aligned with the strategy.

Project information and structuring

The project information and structuring are obtained from the business case report discussed in the previous chapter.

Expert panel

Lenders may use a panel of independent experts to assist in the due diligence. They include the market analyst, project expert, technical expert, and possibly a common or lead counsel. Each lender will have her own legal counsel. Depending on the type of project, lenders may appoint other experts such as for opinions on environmental assessment or a local legal counsel familiar with the laws of a developing country.

The market analyst provides a report on the reasonableness of the sponsors' market analysis. For large private projects, lenders require pre-lease commitments as evidence of good demand before approving the loan. For PPP projects, pre-construction off-take commitments serve a similar purpose.

The project expert provides inputs on all aspects of project management such as scope, preliminary schedule, cost estimates, design management, expected quality, procurement strategy, and project execution.

The technical expert provides an independent review of the specifications, scale, and technology. During the construction phase, the technical expert provides inputs on technical issues that may crop up.

The common or lead counsel of the syndicate provides inputs on the draft project contracts and agreements by the sponsors (i.e., borrower) and other legal opinion. If the project is in a developing country, there are likely to be legal issues regarding contracts, property rights, and their enforcement. The lead counsel should set forth the basis of her actions with the counsels representing the other lenders through a prior representative letter (Ryan, 2009).

From these inputs, lenders may ask for adjustments to the financial model, such as changes to demand projections, costs, schedule, and even the basic engineering technology. If both parties are satisfied with the proposed changes, the next step is to negotiate the terms of the loan.

Loan negotiation

The following terms are likely to be negotiated:

- quantum of loan;
- equity;
- use of subordinated debt (shareholders' loans) as part of equity;
- loan profile;
- sponsors' contingent equity support for cost overrun;
- restrictions; and
- default triggers.

The maximum amount of loan depends largely on the ability of the project to generate sufficient operating profit to cover debt repayment. This ratio should be greater than 1, and lenders often require at least 1.2. Lenders will roll up interest during construction as part of the loan quantum.

Generally, infrastructure projects are financed with about 10 to 40 percent equity. The use of third party equity such as from pension or infrastructure funds is not uncommon in project finance, either directly or indirectly as convertible debt. Sponsors usually provide subordinated debt rather than equity to reduce their taxes. However, these shareholders' loans are often considered as equity. Lenders will want to ensure that interest rates on such loans are reasonable, and payable only after lenders give their permission for payment of dividends to shareholders. Usually, this occurs only after the first repayment of the project loan and the debt-service cover ratio is healthy. In other words, lenders do not want sponsors to extract profits from the project in the form of interest on shareholder loans or dividends too early, before the project stabilizes its operations.

The loan profile contains the mechanics of the loan provided in the Loan Agreement (see next section). It includes the first draw, the periodic draws, grace period, and first repayment. The loan is often available for the first draw after financial close. The periodic draws may be monthly or quarterly. Monthly draws will coincide with contractor's request for progress payment while quarterly disbursements will reduce the paperwork. During the grace period, there is no repayment or just the repayment of interest. Upon the completion of construction, the project takes several months or even up to a year to ramp up to full capacity. During this period, the project is not generating stable revenue and there is usually a grace period.

Sponsors will be required to provide contingent equity support for cost overrun. Normally, the loan does not cover cost overrun although this may be negotiated. This is a reason why scope creep, variation orders, and other factors that raise project costs cannot be taken lightly.

There will be restrictions on the borrower such as profit distribution (i.e. declaration of dividends), further borrowings, capital investment, leasing, and sale of shares. This is to ensure that the borrower has the ability to repay the loan.

The final item to negotiate is default triggers set out in the Common Terms Agreement. As discussed in the previous chapter, one consequence of default is the right of lenders to step in to cure the project. Lenders may replace the management if the project is in serious trouble, which is not in the interest of sponsors.

After negotiation, the agreed terms will be documented in various financial agreements discussed below (Khan and Parra, 2003). Further changes after the signing of these documents will be recorded in a separate Amendment and Waiver Agreement.

Financial agreements

Loan agreement

The Loan Agreement contains the loan schedule and reserved discretions. The loan schedule include the principal, term of loan, amortization period, rate of interest, fees, and interest adjustments.

Reserved discretions are items that require lenders' approval. They include

- termination or transfer of any project agreement;
- decisions to initiate arbitration;
- demands for payment, e.g. payment to contractor;
- assignment of rights or interests;
- issuance of project completion certificate; and
- major contractual variations.

Security agreement

This agreement contains the security package for the project to address the possibility of project failure. It may include

- first charge on mortgage over project land and properties;
- charges on movable assets;
- sponsors' support, e.g. contingent funds, pledge of shares and SPV accounts, completion guarantee, and parent company guarantee;
- assignment of benefits from major project contracts such as purchase and license payments, performance bond proceeds, and liquidated damages backed by Letter of Credit;
- assignment of insurance proceeds and non-parent guarantees such as a Partial Risk Guarantee provided by the World Bank to lenders against political risk; and
- loan covenants (see section on "Common Terms Agreement").

Enforcing security may be an issue. For example, mortgage laws may be weak in developing countries, the concept of charges is not applicable in many countries, and grantors may object to the assignment of PPP contract benefits to lenders.

To secure insurance proceeds, lenders need to control the insurance package such as through the choice of insurer, nature and extent of cover, and assignment of benefits to lenders even if the policyholder breaches policy conditions.

Equity support agreement

In this agreement, sponsors agree to

- provide base equity of about 20 to 40 percent;
- provide project completion guarantee to lenders;
- provide contingent funds for cost overrun; and
- repay all debts if they abandon the project.

Common terms agreement

This agreement between lenders and the SPV deals with

- disbursement and payment;
- conditions precedent;
- representations and warranties;
- covenants; and
- default.

The disbursement and payment section contains items related to draw-downs, repayment, grace period, fees, and prepayment. Lenders charge fees to cover their cost of administering the loan, as well as a commitment fee over the undisbursed balance of the loan.

Before disbursing the loans, lenders require that certain conditions must be met, such as the delivery of project contracts and agreements, security documents, legal opinion on validity and enforcement of these documents, initial deposit of base equity, and payment of lending fees.

The disbursement, such as to the contractor, requires certification by the SPV's auditor and lenders' technical adviser on project cost and progress. For project works in progress, a request for progress payment requires certification by the specialist consultant, cost consultant, and project manager.

The SPV is required to warrant basic facts on its creditworthiness. These representations may include its corporate status, non-default status, non-creation of additional security on project assets, fair financial statements and financial soundness, and environmental compliance.

The loan covenants that require compliance include the use free cash flow, inspection and reporting, and other matters. On free cash flow, the SPV is required to maintain project accounts (see Project Accounts Agreement), ensure adequate cover ratios, and furnish annual operating budget for lenders' approval. The agreement may provide for higher repayment ("cash sweep") if the project has adequate free cash flow. Conversely, if the project falters, there may be a "Clawback clause" for investors to return dividends or other cash deficiency provisions to provide additional funds.

There are also negative covenants spelling out what the SPV must not do, such as not to distribute profits without ensuring debt repayment and fully funded cash trap accounts, that is, sinking funds and debt service reserve.

The following items normally require lenders' approval:

- disposal of major assets;
- major investment;
- further borrowings;
- change of business;
- setting up of subsidiaries;
- transfer of shares; and
- execution of contracts other than approved project documents.

Lenders have the right to inspect project assets and records. The special purpose vehicle (SPV) must furnish audited financial statements and construction progress reports certified by the lenders' technical adviser.

The other matters include payment of taxes, maintenance of insurance, and project compliance with regulatory requirements.

Finally, default triggers include non-payment of debt, failure to comply with equity commitment, failure to pay third parties, misrepresentation, insolvency, non-compliance with covenants, and government actions such as appropriation. For remedies, there is a short cure period beyond which lenders may stop the loan and demand payment, step in to run the project, or sell assets to recover the loan.

Accounts agreement

This agreement provides for the setting up of several accounts in order of priority on use of revenue:

- operations;
- major maintenance (sinking fund);
- debt service payment;
- debt service reserve;
- debt service payment on subordinated debt, if any;
- debt service reserve on subordinated debt, if any;
- voluntary prepayment, if any;
- capital investment; and
- restricted payments (e.g., dividends).

The priority is important because if there is insufficient revenue, then it is unlikely that dividends will be payable.

The accounts may be handled by a trustee who is usually a senior lender in the syndicate, that is, the accounts bank. From the lenders' perspective, letting the SPV handle the accounts creates a lot administrative work and is less secure for debt repayment.

Inter-creditor agreement

This is an agreement among lenders in the syndicate on how to conduct their business. The main provisions include each lender's share of the syndicated loan, order of drawdowns, allocation of debt service repayments, default, approval of SPV's operating budget, and how to deal with changes or requests from the SPV. For example, the SPV may wish to issue a bond to refinance the project, and this requires lenders' approval.

Finalization of project documents

Lenders may require changes to specific clauses in project documents to mitigate certain risks. Clearly, these changes will need to be negotiated and, once agreed, the documents will be finalized.

Hedging arrangements

Recall that hedging instruments include Interest rate swaps, currency swaps, futures contracts, and forward contracts. Lenders will want to ensure that appropriate hedging instruments are in place.

Financial close

Once the conditions precedent to a loan have been satisfied, lenders and sponsors will reach a financial deal. This ensures that everything is in order, including the PPP contract, permits and approvals, project contracts and agreements, and insurances.

Refinancing

Upon completion of construction, sponsors may seek to refinance the loan at a lower rate of interest because construction risk has been eliminated. One way is to renegotiate the loan with the existing lender.

Another possibility is for the SPV to issue bonds, which incurs issuance costs but, more importantly, is less flexible when it comes to renegotiating with many investors such as if the project runs into serious trouble.

A third refinancing approach is for the SPV to secure a new loan from long-term investors such as insurers, infrastructure funds, and pension funds.

Securitization

Lenders may not want to hold on to project loans because of the long duration, which may extend up to 40 years. There is a clear mismatch between long-term loans and short-term deposits. In some countries, such as the US, the lender provides a land and construction loan and, upon completion of construction, a permanent lender such as an insurer takes over the loan. However, such loans are uncommon; it is more usual for a lender to provide long-term rather than take-out financing.

Loan securitization offers a solution to overcome the mismatch of loans and deposits. The originating lender sells the loans to a special purpose entity (SPE) set up by a sponsor. The securitization SPE, not to be confused with the project SPV, issues securities to investors to obtain the funds to pay the originators. The originators may then use the funds to finance new projects or for some other purposes. In addition to improving liquidity, the originator no longer assumes project risks because it no longer owns the loans to earn interest income.

The SPV (borrower) will continue with periodic repayments of the loan to the originator. In turn, the originator, for a small fee, will forward these repayments to a trustee (the paying agency, which is just another financial institution), to pay investors.

The SPE pools (buys) project loans from different types of projects from originators. These loans are then categorized into tranches (e.g. Class A, B, and C) with varying risk profiles and priorities of payments and hence different interest rates. These rates are normally quoted in terms of the spread over a benchmark rate such as the Singapore Interbank Offered Rate (SIBOR). Investors select the tranche(s) that suit(s) their risk appetite. The bulk of the securities will be Class A grade, which is less risky. Other possible credit enhancements to attract investors include acquiring the following:

- insurance against default by borrowers on investment grade securities;
- ratings on securities;
- repurchase agreements with originators to buy back affected loans;
- warranties by originators against certain project risks;
- interest rate swaps to convert floating to fixed rates;
- participation by originators, especially in purchase of Class C securities;
- sale of loans by originators at a discount;
- currency swaps to mitigate currency risks if original loans are in different currencies; and
- making securities tradable in the secondary market.

Investors will bear other risks such as delays in payments and non-performance by the parties such as the originator, trustee, and sponsor of SPE. Normally, the SPE appoints a servicer to do the administration and processing. The servicer may not perform.

Investors will have to do their homework on the above credit enhancements, project quality, size of the pool of projects, whether construction has been completed at time of securitization, and so on. As the subprime mortgage crisis has shown, securitization can go badly wrong (Mullo and Padilla, 2009; Schultz and Fabozzi, 2016).

References

Harris, D. (1974) Credit rationing at commercial banks: Some empirical evidence. *Journal of Money, Credit and Banking*, 6(2), 227–240.

Khan, F. and Parra, R. (2003) *Financing large projects*. New York: Pearson.

Mullo, P. and Padilla, M. (2009) *Chain of blame: How Wall Street caused the mortgage and credit crisis*. New York: Wiley.

Ryan, R. (2009) The role of lead counsel in syndicated lending transactions. *The Business Lawyer*, 64(3), 783–800.

Schultz, G. and Fabozzi, F. (2016) *Investing in mortgage-backed and asset-backed securities*. New York: Wiley.

CHAPTER 10

Sponsor's pre-construction activities

Establishment of special purpose vehicle

The next step after financial close is for sponsors to establish the special purpose vehicle (SPV). Sponsors have different ways to structure their working relations (Table 10.1), and the form, liability, and taxation will differ depending on tax jurisdictions. The parent company is not directly involved in running the project because of liability and other risks in different countries such as local ownership requirements and restrictions on property transactions. Further, lenders want sponsors to set up an SPV to ring-fence the project revenues and cash flows as security for the loan.

A common mode for project financing is the limited liability company (LLC) because of limited liability and avoidance of corporate double taxation on profit and dividend. An alternative arrangement is a limited liability partnership (LLP) where there is no general partner but limited partners still exercise management control.

Joint ventures (JVs) and consortia are unincorporated, and the word "consortium" normally refers to larger ventures. The parties do not set up an SPV but regulate their relations through a JV agreement. It stipulates their equity and other contributions, the management structure, liability, profit sharing, ownership of intellectual property, possible restraints on behavior outside the JV, when and how the JV will end, and dispute resolution. Taxation is often based on "pass through" basis, that is, the parties to the JV agreement will file their own tax. The JV is seldom used in project financing because lenders will want to "ring fence" repayment sources.

The incorporation is usually in a low-tax country such as the British Virgin Islands (BVI) where it is easier to manage tax and other matters such as avoidance of double taxation, minimal disclosure and reporting

Table 10.1   Types of investment vehicles.

Investment vehicle	Liability	Taxation
Incorporated		
Corporation	Limited	Profit and dividend
Limited liability company	Limited	Income tax
Partnership		
General partner	Unlimited	Income tax
Limited partner	Limited	Income tax
Unincorporated		
Joint venture	Unlimited	Pass through
Consortium	Unlimited	Pass through

requirements, and flexibility in profit distribution. A project company pays tax where it operates, not where it is incorporated. Hence, a BVI-incorporated company does not avoid paying tax in the country of operation. If a parent company has projects in different countries, it is likely to set up a passive holding company in a low-tax country to consolidate multiple sources of income.

As discussed in Chapter 7, the Development Agreement will serve as a basis for the Shareholders' Agreement. As security for the project loan, sponsors may pledge their shares to lenders. They retain ownership and hence the privileges such as management, voting rights, and dividends. If sponsors default on the loan, lenders may sell the shares or exercise voting rights on the pledged shares, such as to replace the management if the project is failing.

Project governance structure and project office

The word "governance" has different meanings. For the World Bank (1994), "good governance" at the country level means having the following attributes:

- effective bureaucracy;
- accountability;

- transparency;
- inclusive development;
- participatory processes;
- active civil society; and
- rule of the law.

At the organization level, corporate governance refers to the system of rules and processes that direct and control a company (Tricker, 2019).

As mentioned in Chapter 3, the project governance structure spells out who has the authority to make decisions to direct and control the project. Typically, there are two levels within the SPV. Management will make the strategic decisions and serve as the approving authority. It issues a project charter to appoint the project team. The team works in the project office and is responsible for the day-to-day execution of the project. It comprises a senior and experienced project manager, in-house members, and consultants. The composition depends on tasks, experience, and expertise. If an organization has many projects, it is likely to set up an enabling project management office (PMO) to develop, coordinate, and standardize procedures (Taylor, 2016).

Project brief

The sponsor or Project Director will brief the project team. The Project Brief often contains the following information:

- project title;
- sponsor;
- goals and objectives;
- scope, design, and performance requirements;
- success criteria;
- site information;
- project governance structure;
- procurement strategy;
- draft contracts and agreements;
- reporting and monitoring;
- key stakeholders;
- regulatory requirements;
- budget, preliminary schedule, and milestones;

- expected quality;
- opportunities and constraints; and
- major risks and mitigation.

The project success (output) criteria often include the technical criteria of time, cost, quality, and safety expectations. In addition, a project must satisfy the business criteria of stakeholder satisfaction and alignment with the business case.

Project schedule

The project team develops the project schedule using a bar chart (Table 10.2). It lists the main activities to undertake up to the start of the operation and maintenance phase.

Table 10.2   Project schedule.

	Period			
	1	2	3	...
Site survey and engineering studies				
Site visits				
Visit similar facilities				
Programming				
Schematic design				
Design development				
Construction documents				
Final review				
Permits and approvals				
Tender				
Award of contract				
Mobilization				
Construction				
Purchase of equipment				
Commissioning				
Occupation				
Staff training				
Start of operation				

Site survey, analysis, and engineering studies

A site survey is necessary to establish legal boundaries, develop contour maps, and subsequently peg the building layouts. The site analysis is similar to that covered in Chapter 4 except that it is the sponsor, rather than the grantor, that carries out the analysis.

The engineering studies will include a geotechnical report and possibly reports on environmental, traffic, town planning, and other community concerns. The grantor may have conducted some of these studies and share them with the SPV, usually on a "for information only" basis without liability. This means that, if necessary, the SPV must do its own due diligence by conducting an independent study.

Programming

We assume that the SPV will design the facility and develop the construction documents for tender. If the project uses Design-Build (DB) or Engineering, Procurement, and Construction (EPC) contracts, the contractor will be responsible for the design. The steps for design development are similar.

Programming refers to the process of gathering project requirements. The project team extracts the basic requirements from the Project Brief. It may visit similar facilities to gather more ideas. Finally, it gathers additional requirements from different stakeholders. To guide this process, the team develops a preliminary work breakdown structure (WBS) and collects requirements for each component.

Design brief

Once the requirements are collated and finalized (approved), the project team develops the Design Brief to guide the design. For example, for a building, the Design Brief consists of narratives and information on the following items:

- project;
- design concept;

- target green rating and simulation requirements;
- life cycle considerations;
- opportunities and constraints;
- building orientation;
- integration with adjacent uses;
- privacy;
- visuals and lines of sight;
- major systems;
- special systems;
- major materials and colors;
- space program;
- use of external spaces;
- landscaping;
- regulatory approvals;
- Building Information Modeling (BIM) requirements;
- equipment and furnishings, including special equipment; and
- design review process.

We assume that the grantor has fixed the design concept during the Public Private Partnership (PPP) tender when requesting for price and design proposals.

For a building, the major systems consist of the structural, civil, mechanical, electrical, energy, plumbing, and technology systems. The latter include building management, security, and information technology systems. Some buildings require special systems; for example, a concert hall will require a proper sound system. The space program divides the building into different spaces each with its data sheet and adjacencies to locate functionally related rooms near each other.

Design management

The project team manages the design process by

- assigning design responsibilities;
- establishing the number of design options to be considered;
- developing progressive cost and schedule estimates;

- managing the design review and approval process;
- performing value engineering and constructability review if necessary;
- managing the regulatory planning, transport, and design approvals; and
- managing the design information.

Normally, a senior in-house or external designer has overall design responsibility. She uses a design work breakdown structure (DWBS) to assign the design of different components to other designers.

In general, sponsors expect designers to generate about three options before approving and finalizing the conceptual or schematic design. As noted earlier, we assume that the grantor has fixed the land-use plan and schematic design during tender by selecting the winning bidder. The next stage is design development, followed by the development of contract documents.

Progressive cost and schedule estimates

As the design develops, the project team will progressively estimate the project cost and schedule with increasing precision. This ensures that the project is designed to budget and can be built within schedule. Table 10.3 shows an example using elemental costing for a building to develop the shadow bid. It provides a benchmark for the SPV to compare subsequent tender bids.

Design reviews

During design development, there are often two design review and approval stages, when the design is at 30% and 90% of completion respectively, to ensure that the design

- adheres to design criteria;
- is within scope;
- meets functional and operational objectives;
- complies with code;

Table 10.3   Elemental cost estimate for a building.

	Estimated cost	Cost/m²	Percentage
Foundation			
Substructure			
Superstructure			
Exterior			
…			
Total direct cost	(1)		
Site overhead	(2)		
Construction cost	(3) = (1) + (2)		
Company overhead	(4)		
Net project cost	(5) = (3) + (4)		
Mark-up @15% of (5)			
Goods and service tax on materials			
Insurance			
Bond			
Estimated tender price			

- is integrated and has compatible interfaces;
- considers safety;
- does not contain conflicts, errors, and omissions; and
- is on schedule.

The design review is also an opportunity to obtain feedback from designers.

Value engineering

The design team may carry out value engineering at the 30% and 60% design stages to provide a leaner design by (Younker, 2003; Huthwaite, 2004)

- removing unnecessary expenditure;
- simplifying methods and procedures;
- removing redundant items;

- considering the use of alternative materials and standards where applicable;
- reducing excess inventory;
- reducing unnecessary transport;
- minimizing defects and rework;
- reducing environmental waste; and
- reducing energy requirements.

Constructability review

Depending on the scale and complexity of projects, there may be a constructability review of the draft bid documents near the end of the design stage by an internal or external team ("a new pair of eyes") to

- ensure conformance with codes;
- remove design conflicts;
- determine if the schedule is realistic;
- ensure that different drawings and documents are coordinated;
- remove errors;
- check for omissions;
- ensure safe construction of the facility.

An improved design will attract better-informed bids from contractors and speed up the construction process.

Regulatory design approvals

The regulatory design approvals often relate to town planning, building, fire, utilities, health, transport, and environmental matters. In many cases, designers submit these plans for approval on behalf of owners.

Managing design information

There are many design drawings and there is a need to develop a system to manage and share the information among relevant parties. The general requirements are to categorize different types of drawings using an appropriate numbering system (e.g. "Axxx" for architectural drawings), keep track of different versions and amendments, and implement a system for dissemination. After design, the information is required for construction, operation, and maintenance.

A paper-based building information system will be costly because it is difficult to organize, update, and retrieve. In the 1980s, some of the paperwork were converted into electronic files but the problems remain. The current preference is to use Building Information Modeling (BIM). To encourage the use of BIM, some countries mandate the submission of plans using BIM for approval.

BIM is a digital representation, "twin" or model of the building. It allows users to view the three-dimensional building (3D BIM) from different angles, the building plans, the elevations and sections, the major systems, and the attributes for each component or object. Importantly, the information in entered only once to avoid inconsistencies. This new information is updated automatically in all representations of the model. By spending time to develop the digital twin, designers hope to reduce design issues on site. BIM has other uses, such as to develop the schedule (4D BIM), progressive cost estimates and control (5D BIM), analysis of building performance such as energy simulation (6D BIM), and operation and maintenance (7D BIM).

Before implementing BIM, the parties need to sort out many commercial, legal, and technical issues (Hardin and McCool, 2015). The commercial and legal concerns include roles and responsibilities, rights to information, liability, insurance, training and capacity, collaboration process, and security of information. The technical issues include object classification, location (coordinates), attribute data, construction tolerances, volume computation, drawing templates, naming conventions, annotations, software versions, data exchange formats, and control over the common data environment.

Commissioning plan

The project team prepares the commissioning plan to test the major systems and equipment. For example, for a building, the systems to be tested include lifts, escalators, air-conditioning, lighting, fire protection, structural system, security, IT systems, and so on. The plan consists of the following (Grondzik, 2009):

- systems to be commissioned;
- whether the commissioning is done by the designers or an external party acceptable to the SPV's project team and contractor;
- commissioning budget;
- risk assessment;
- special resources required; and
- commissioning schedule.

Development of contract documents

As the design proceeds, it will be necessary to capture the design intent as part of the contract documents. These contract documents include the specifications and drawings. We will briefly discuss the documents in the next section.

Tender documents

The construction tender documents consist of the following:

- Invitation to Tender;
- Instructions to Bidders;
- Bid Form;
- Form of Agreement;
- Form of Bond (performance bond);
- General Conditions of Contract;
- Special Conditions of Contract;
- Drawings and specifications;
- Schedule of Basic Rates;
- Bills of Quantities (if any); and
- Addenda.

The General Conditions of Contract contain common contract clauses. A project may have special clauses and they are found in the Special Conditions of Contract. Each specification has three elements, namely,

- the product;
- the standards or certifications required; and
- the standard of workmanship, testing, training, and other requirements.

Bidders will fill in the Schedule of Basic Rates as part of the tender for subsequent use in pricing variations orders. The project team is likely to renegotiate the rates before awarding the construction contract. If the Bills of Quantities are provided, contractors will use them to price their tenders. Finally, the Addenda contains any last-minute changes to the tender documents.

Tender process

The tender process to select the contractor is similar to the grantor's tender process. It begins with pre-qualification, followed by invitation to tender, pre-bid conference, receipt of bids, evaluation, negotiation, and award of contract. The pre-qualification criteria are similar, such as, experience, technical expertise, financial resources, history of litigation, and contractual non-performance (Asian Development Bank, 2018).

Contractor's decision to bid and planning

If it is not a Design-Build project, the contractor will decide whether he will bid for the project by examining its workload, labor conditions, project prestige, reputation of sponsors and designers, number of bidders, risk allocation, contractual terms, safety, possible site problems, performance bond capacity, and quality of contract documents.

Next, the contractor will

- visit the site;
- attend the pre-bid meeting;
- work out the "methods statement" on how to build the facility;
- develop a preliminary Work Breakdown Structure;
- develop a preliminary schedule;

- develop a preliminary cost estimate based on Table 10.3 or something similar;
- decide what to subcontract and obtain respective suppliers' and sub-contractors' bids;
- raise queries or obtain further information from the sponsor's project team;
- prepare the bid; and
- submit the bid.

The sequence of activities may vary; for example, the sponsor dictates the timing of the site visit.

If the design of a component is not complete at the time of tender, contractors will be asked to put a *provisional sum* for that item in the bid. If it is work or material to be supplied by a nominated subcontractor, the contractor will put it as a *prime cost sum* in the bid. The contractor has her own domestic subcontractors. A sponsor may nominate a subcontractor for certain specialized jobs. The contractor will assist the nominated sub-contractor on site, such as for coordination, lifting of goods, and supply of utilities. Hence, the contractor is entitled to mark-up and attendance.

References

Asian Development Bank (2018) *Prequalification*. Manila: ADB.

Grondzik, W. (2009) *Principles of building commissioning*. New York: Wiley.

Hardin, B. and McCool, D. (2015) *BIM and construction management*. New York: Wiley.

Huthwaite, B. (2004) *The lean design solution*. Michigan: Institute for Lean Innovation.

Taylor, P. (2016) *Leading successful PMOs*. London: Routledge.

Tricker, B. (2019) *Corporate governance*. London: Oxford University Press.

World Bank (1994) *Governance: The World Bank experience*. Washington DC: World Bank.

Younker, D. (2003) *Value engineering*. London: CRC Press.

CHAPTER 11

Mobilization

Notice to proceed

The Notice to Proceed (NTP) is a formal letter from the sponsor informing the contractor to start work.

The NTP marks the beginning of the contract period, as distinct from the earlier date of signing of contract. The reason for the two dates is that the sponsor may not be ready for the contractor to start work, in which case she may issue a Notice of Intent. The contractor will also need to apply for various permits from the regulatory authorities before starting work. We assume that designers have obtained town planning and building plan approvals. During the construction phase, the contractor will need to apply for demolition, greenery (e.g. tree relocation), traffic, drainage, used water, sewage, waste disposal, fire, and pest control approvals.

Submittals and baseline plans

The NTP is conditional on the contractor's submission of performance bond, insurances (see Chapter 7), list of subcontractors and suppliers, as well as the project schedule and other baseline plans to the sponsor. Recall that the sponsor has worked out her communications, commissioning, and risk management plans. We will discuss the contractor's baseline plans later in this chapter.

The performance bond is about 10 percent of the contract sum. The surety or bonding company will pay the sponsor if the contractor does not perform and then seeks to recover the sum from the contractor. The bond normally extends until the end of defects liability period, which is usually one year after the completion of construction. The performance bond is callable depending on whether the sponsor needs to prove the contractor's breach of contract. If proof is required, it is a conditional bond; otherwise, it is an on-demand bond. Obviously, sponsors prefer on-demand bonds.

Kick-off meeting

The kick-off meeting is the first meeting for the sponsor's project team to brief the contractor's project team. The key subcontractors may also attend the kick-off meeting if the subcontracts have been awarded. The agenda includes

- brief project information covering the rationale for the project, sponsor(s), and goals and objectives;
- key stakeholders;
- partnering agreement, if any;
- project scope;
- broad schedule and milestones;
- success criteria (see "Project Brief" in Chapter 10);
- constraints;
- roles of team members and communication lines; and
- procedures such as change orders, commissioning, and progress payment.

A "partnering agreement" among key stakeholders spells out the project's goals and objectives, the commitment to work together in the spirit of trust and openness, and timely resolution of disputes (Godfrey, 1996). When the commercial stakes are high, the parties are more likely to regulate their relations by contract if they do not have equal bargaining power. While top management may sign a partnering agreement, perceptions at the project level may be different.

Award of subcontracts

Depending on the sequence of construction, the contractor will proceed to award subcontracts according to the sequence of construction. Generally, there will be flow-through clauses from the main contract to the subcontracts.

Procurement

The contractor will need to procure equipment, materials, and workers. Long-lead items such as specialty equipment, custom-made components or systems, and imported items should be procured early to avoid supply disruptions and delays. We will discuss the contractor's procurement plan later in the chapter.

Site organization and staffing plan

In organizing the site, the contractor needs to take into account site constraints that affect connection to utilities, jobsite safety, signage, security, ingress and egress routes, movement of materials and component, storage, productivity of workers, use of equipment, location of site office, rest area, and temporary facilities, and environmental control measures.

Cranes require overhead rights such as over property, roads, and power lines to move materials. However, third parties may not grant these rights, thereby restricting movements to within the site boundary. Because of site constraints, the use of "just-in-time" materials delivery (Ohno, 1988) requires the coordination of construction, crane, and delivery schedules. The contractor will also plan for affected areas outside the site, such as pedestrian and vehicular traffic.

The staffing arrangement is given in Table 11.1. There are many variations depending on the complexity and size of the project.

Table 11.1   Contractor's staffing arrangement.

	Responsibilities
Head Office	Contract administration, cost estimation
Project manager	Overall in charge, liaise with designers, and reports to Head Office
Superintendent	Site activities
Assistant superintendent	Subcontractors and suppliers
Office manager	Documents, accounts, purchasing, and so on
Project engineer	Field engineering and project control
BIM manager	Building Information Modeling (BIM) coordination
Health and safety officer	Site health and safety
General foreman	Foremen of different trades

Construction schedule

Recall from Chapter 7 that the sponsor has a broad project schedule with milestones. The contractor will submit a more detailed schedule to the sponsor as a contractual requirement. The sponsor's project team uses the schedule to monitor construction progress.

The contractor's project team develops the schedule by creating a precedence diagram (Table 11.2) from the work breakdown structure (WBS) and using it to identify the critical path. In practice, there will be many activities (or work packages) and we use a simple example to illustrate how to identify the critical path. It is important to identify the activities, predecessors, and durations accurately.

The next step is to use the arrow diagrams (Figs. 11.1 and 11.2) to determine the *critical path*. The convention is as follows:

ES	Activity	EF
LS	Duration	LF

Here ES is early start, LS is late start, EF is early finish, and LF is late finish. The forward pass begins with activity A and continues until activity F. Observe that F has two predecessors and can only start on Week 12.

The backward pass begins with activity F, starting with LF = 14 weeks, the project duration. We then work backwards to compute LF and LS for activities D and E. For activity C, LF is the minimum of (LS D, LS E) = min (7, 11) = 7. Similarly, for activity A, LF = min (LS B, LS C) = min (3, 5) = 3. The critical path consists of activities with EF = LF, that is, A-B-D-F. Any

Table 11.2   Precedence diagram.

Activity	Predecessor	Duration (weeks)
A	—	3
B	A	4
C	A	2
D	B, C	5
E	C	1
F	D, E	2

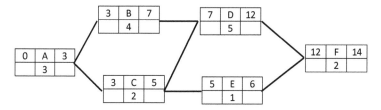

Fig. 11.1   Forward pass.

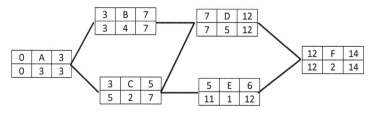

Fig. 11.2   Backward pass.

delay in a critical path activity will delay the entire project. The critical path may be different if the durations change, that is, another "near" critical path may become critical. For activities not on the critical path, LF − EF = LS − ES is the slack or float. For example, activity C can start as early as Week 3 or as late as Week 5.

The final step in preparing the schedule is to develop a bar or Gantt chart using the early start timings (Table 11.3). A boldface "**x**" indicates critical path activities. Activities C and E are not on critical path and have floats ("f").

Resource plan

For each activity, the team estimates the key equipment (e.g. crane), labor, materials, and subcontractors required (Table 11.4).

In each category, we can create sub-categories using additional rows. For example, we can create sub-categories of cranes and machinery for "equipment" and each cell will show the number of each equipment required for the week. Similarly, each key subcontractor may occupy a

Table 11.3   Project schedule.

Task ID	Description	Duration	Week													
			1	2	3	4	5	6	7	8	9	10	11	12	13	14
1	A	3	x		x	x										
2	B	4		x		x	x		x	x						
3	C	2		x		x	x		f	f						
4	D	5							x		x	x		x	x	
5	E	1					x		x	f		f	f		f	f
6	F	2											x	x		x

Table 11.4   Project schedule and resources.

Task ID	Description	Duration	Week													
			1	2	3	4	5	6	7	8	9	10	11	12	13	14
1	A	3	x		x	x										
2	B	4		x		x	x		x	x						
3	C	2				x	x		x	f						
4	D	5							x		x	x		x	x	
5	E	1					x		x	f		f	f		f	f
6	F	2											x	x		x
	Equipment		2	2	3	3										
	Labor		5	5	6	6	5	5	4	4	4	4	3	3	3	3
	Materials						4	3	3	3	3	3	2	2		
	Subcon Y					x	x									
							x									
	Subcon Z						x									
							x									

row, as shown for subcontractors Y and Z. The numbers for labor refer to key personnel, and that for materials are for illustration only, in appropriate units.

In this example, the contractor has subcontracted activity C to subcontractor Y and activity E to subcontractor Z. However, subcontractor Y cannot start in Week 3 as originally planned because he has to go to another project site. Hence, activity C will start in Week 4 and end in Week 6, giving only one week of float. This process of rescheduling activities because of resource constraints is called *resource leveling*. Sometimes, it is not possible to develop a workable schedule. In this case, we may shorten the durations of some activities by *crashing*, that is, by providing additional resources to accelerate work. The activities to crash will also depend on cost implications.

The sponsor may have some concerns on a contractor's schedule. For example, if many activities have late starts, there is a higher risk of delaying the project. However, the contractor may not be willing to change the schedule because of cost and other implications. There are three positions on this matter (Rubin *et al.*, 1999):

- the contractor has the right because the schedule is a basis for pricing his bid;
- the sponsor has the right because, ultimately, he pays for everything; or
- the float is allocated on first-come-first-served basis to the party that has a legitimate reason to use it.

On the third position, if the contractor experiences a delay on a critical activity, he may want to reschedule a non-critical activity, that is, use the float. Similarly, if the sponsor causes a delay on a non-critical activity, he will want to avoid paying damages by arguing that the activity is not on the critical path and has float.

Unfortunately, in our case of a contractor submitting a risky schedule, it is unclear who owns the float. The obvious solution is to be explicit about it in the contract. When the contract is vague or silent, such disputes may arise.

Budget and cost systems

The contractor converts his estimate of the bid into a project budget for the work packages. He then submits a schedule of values (SOV) to the sponsor on the expected amount of progress payment for each period. This allows the sponsor and lender to set aside the required sum.

To construct the SOV, the contractor first lists the work packages (WP) (Table 11.5); for example, WP "A" is the foundation, and WP "B" is the substructure. For each WP, the contractor estimates the labor, materials, and equipment costs. Observe that WP "B" is subcontracted. The sum of all WPs is the direct cost. The contractor then adds the indirect costs comprising site overhead, company overhead, mark-up, goods and services tax (GST) on materials, insurance, and bond. The total cost is $140 m, which is the contract value. To convert the direct costs to values, he multiplies each row subtotal by the ratio of contract value to direct cost, that is, by 140/100.

The next step is to spread each WP value over its duration using the project schedule in Table 11.4. For example, he may spread the $14 m for WP "A" into $6 m, $4 m, and $4 m over the three weeks. The SOV is then the column sum of each period. The contractor submits Table 11.6 to the sponsor. He does not show his costs and workings, particularly the profit margin. From the SOV, the sponsor knows that he has to set aside $20 m in the first period, $15 m in the second period, and so on.

Table 11.5   Computation of work package values.

WP	Labor	Materials	Equipment	Subcontract	Subtotal	Value ($m)
A	4	3	3		10	14
B				5	5	7
etc.					...	...
			Direct cost		100	
			Site overhead			
			Company overhead			
			Mark-up			
			GST on materials			
			Insurance			
			Bond			
			Contract value		140	140

Table 11.6   Schedule of values.

WP	Value ($m)	Period			
		1	2	3	...
A	14				
B	7				
...	...				
Total	140	20	15	12	...

Quality plan

Quality is often defined as meeting or exceeding customers' requirements and expectations. There are four levels of quality with corresponding approaches and principles or tools (Table 11.7).

TQM focuses on a set of principles at company and project levels to improve quality. These principles include

- quality as part of corporate strategy to compete effectively;
- leadership that provides direction, objectives, support, and manage resistance;
- providing an effective organization structure for quality improvement;
- systems or holistic approach to quality;
- customer focus and thorough understanding of customer requirements;
- employee involvement and empowerment;
- process approach to quality;
- continuous improvement or kaizen (Imai, 2012);
- productive maintenance;
- evidence-based decision-making; and
- cultivating win-win supplier and subcontractor relations.

Quality assurance focuses on the process level, such as improving a contractor's bid preparation, tender process, project planning, and so on.

Table 11.7   Quality levels and approaches.

Level	Quality approach	Principles or tools
Company	Total quality management (TQM)	Principles (see text)
Project	TQM	Principles (see text)
Process	Quality assurance (QA)	PDCA cycle, six sigma, re-engineering, failure mode and effect analysis, certification, etc.
Product or service	Quality control (QC)	Cause and effect diagram, Pareto diagram, checklists, inspections, tests, samples, control charts, scatter diagram, etc.

Finally, at the product or service level, quality control aims to reduce defects and variability.

There are many tools for improving quality. For example, in the Plan-Do-Check-Act (PDCA) cycle, the planning phase consists of

- defining the process;
- developing the flow chart; and
- documenting the process.

The "doing" phase consists of

- evaluating the process;
- ascertaining the causes such as design, process, equipment, materials, finishing, inspection, testing, packaging, or worker; and
- finding new solutions.

The proposed solutions are then "checked" for effectiveness before "acting" on it, that is, implementation and evaluation. Readers can read up books on TQM for other tools (e.g. Kiran, 2016).

Risk management plan

Recall from Chapter 3 that the grantor normally assumes political and regulatory risks and allocates commercial risks to the SPV. In turn, the

SPV allocates construction or completion risks to the contractor. In addition, both parties may share force majeure risks that are beyond their control. Hence, the contractor's risk management plan focuses on project planning and execution.

The risk management process consists of

- identifying the risks;
- prioritizing the risks by assessing likelihoods and impacts;
- developing mitigation measures; and
- monitoring and review.

For the contractor, the main risks relate to (Greiman, 2013)

- unclear or misunderstanding of project scope;
- unexpected site conditions;
- cost, e.g. poor bid estimate, unforeseen cost changes, and failure keep within budget;
- time, e.g. poor estimates of task durations, sequencing, and coordination;
- quality, e.g. defects;
- safety;
- labor issues;
- unfamiliarity with new technologies;
- unfamiliarity with local conditions or practices;
- design errors and omissions, if the contractor is also responsible for design;
- procurement, e.g. non-performance of suppliers and subcontractors;
- cash flow, such as payment issues; and
- difficulties in settling disputes, including insurance claims.

For each risk, it is possible to assess the consequence or risk exposure, which is defined as likelihood of occurrence x impact. Usually, a 5-point scale is used to rate the likelihood and impact of a risk event. Risk events are then ranked by their consequences, as illustrated in Table 3.3.

Recall from Chapter 3 (Table 3.4) that there are a number of risk mitigation strategies. Finally, there is a need to monitor and periodically conduct risk reviews. As the project progresses, risks may change.

Contractor's procurement plan

The contactor's procurement plan deals with the appointment of subcontractors and purchases of goods and services. Contractors use their network of subcontractors and suppliers. For purchases, the site or engineering team makes a proposal to the procurement department. The latter

- approves the proposal;
- prepares the purchase contract;
- searches for potential suppliers;
- conducts the tender;
- analyzes the bids;
- prepares the purchase order; and
- monitors progress such as requirement for test certificates and shipping.

For imports, the standard shipping terms are free on board (FOB) and cost, insurance and freight (CIF). These are international commerce terms (incoterms). FOB is cheaper as the seller is responsible only to the point where the item is loaded onto a ship. Once the ship sails, the buyer assumes the costs and liabilities. In a CIF arrangement, the seller is responsible until the buyer receives the item, that is, up to the project site or factory gate. The preferred arrangement is likely to depend on whether the seller is familiar with local customs, taxes, and transport conditions.

Sponsors do not require submission of the contractor's procurement plan. However, they do require the contractor to submit a list of subcontractors.

Safety and health plan

Recall from Chapter 10 that designers need to design for safety. Similarly, the contractor has a safety plan to build safely. The plan consists of

- a general policy statement of management commitment and that everyone is responsible for safety;
- safety organization structure for assigning responsibility, monitoring, and reporting;

Table 11.8   Contractor's documentation plan.

Project stage	Folders/Documents
Tender	Tender documents, subcontracts
Mobilization	Permits and approvals, baseline plans, bond, insurance
Construction	Cost and status reports, submittals, variation orders, claims and disputes, tests and inspections, progress payments, work certification, progress reports, procurement
Project close-out	Commissioning test results, punch list, certificates, final documents, training of operatives, project evaluation, post-occupancy audit

- systematic identification of hazards;
- safety standards, e.g. fall protection, demolition, ergonomics, preventing heat stress, and protective gear;
- mitigation measures;
- briefing, communication, safety signs, and training;
- site safety rules;
- incident management; and
- safety requirements for subcontractors and other external parties.

Safety and health thinking require a holistic approach to planning and execution (Moran, 2003; Goh, 2021).

Documentation plan

The contractor's documentation plan shows the documents and folders at each stage of the project cycle (Table 11.8).

Social and environmental management plan

For most infrastructure projects, the grantor is responsible for the social aspects relating to land acquisition, resettlement, and environmental resistance. The grantor is also required to mitigate environmental damage or delegate it to the sponsor. The latter will price in the additional cost in the bid.

For the contractor, the environmental management plan consists of the following:

- statement of commitment;
- roles and responsibilities;
- regulatory requirements;
- list of site-specific environmental issues;
- mitigation measures;
- emergency response plan;
- induction and training;
- incident management;
- non-conformance and rectification;
- monitoring plan;
- audit; and
- improvement.

The contractor's environment officer will coordinate with the sponsor's counterpart to integrate the environmental plans.

The list of site-specific environmental issues includes

- air quality;
- noise;
- soil erosion and sediment control;
- water management;
- land management;
- fire management;
- hazardous materials;
- waste management;
- protection of plants, trees, and animals;
- pest control; and
- reinstatement, if necessary.

Inspection plan

The sponsor's project team will want to inspect certain aspects of the construction. The inspection plan sorts out the inspection protocol. It comprises the following:

- the items to inspect;
- inspector's qualifications;
- limits to inspector authority;
- testing procedures;
- hold points and documentation;
- acceptance procedures;
- procedure for resolving disputes;
- inspection reports; and
- issuance of inspection certificate.

A "hold point" is a point where the contractor cannot cover without proper inspection, such as in pouring concrete to erect a building column.

Table 11.9   Contractor's communications plan.

Mode	Purpose	Attendees	Chair/ author	Means	Frequency
Kick-off meeting	Introduce project	Project team, subcontractors	PM	Meeting	Start of project
Status report	Update management	—	PM	Email	Monthly
Project team meetings	Review progress & take action	Project team	PM	Meeting	Weekly
Project Advisory Group meeting	Update and resolve issues before escalating to sponsor	PM, Project Advisory Group	PM	Meeting	Monthly
Sponsor meeting	Update and resolve issues	Sponsor's project team, contractor's project team	PM	Meeting	Monthly
External stakeholders' meeting	Inform, resolve issues		PM	Meeting	ad hoc
Debrief	Post-project review	Project team, subcontractors	PM	Meeting	End of project
Debrief	Post-project review	Project team, sponsor	Sponsor's PM	Meeting	End of project

Table 11.10   Stakeholder management plan.

Stakeholder	Interest	Priority	Modes of engagement
Grantor	Project completion	Keep informed	Through SPV
Special Purpose Vehicle (SPV)	Project completion	Manage closely	Project meetings
SPV's lender	Project completion	Keep informed	Through SPV
Operator	Project completion	Keep informed	Through SPV
Subcontractors	Prompt payment, good working relations	Manage closely	Project meetings
Suppliers	Prompt payment, good working relations	Manage closely	Project meetings
Customers/users	Project completion	Manage closely	Meetings
Community	Traffic, noise, etc.	Keep informed	Periodic updates
Mass media	General public issues	Keep informed	Periodic updates
Pressure groups	Social, environmental, and other issues	Keep informed	Periodic updates
Internal	Project completion	Manage closely	Internal modes

The consulting engineer or her representative will want to see that the reinforcement bars are in place.

Communications plan

The contractor's communications plan shows the mode of communication, purpose, attendees, chair or author(s), means of dissemination, and frequency (Table 11.9).

The communications plan is not only about information exchange. It is an opportunity to build trust, generate support, manage change and resistance, mitigate conflict, and facilitate stakeholders' satisfaction (Plowman and Diffendal, 2020).

Stakeholder management plan

Just like the grantor and sponsor, the contractor needs a plan to manage stakeholders (Table 11.10). Stakeholder management is about understanding their concerns (interests) and taking steps to resolve these issues.

Commissioning plan

The contractor integrates the commissioning with the sponsor's plan (see Chapter 10). It covers the following (Grondzik, 2009):

- commissioning budget;
- commissioning team (internal or external);
- systems to be commissioned;
- risk assessment;
- special resources required;
- commissioning schedule;
- acceptance criteria;
- documentation;
- training of operatives; and
- issuance of certificates.

   The systems to be commissioned include power, lighting, HVAC (heating, ventilation and air conditioning), refrigeration, plumbing, fire, communications, computer, security, vertical transport, waste disposal, building envelope, structural, and special systems.

References

Godfrey, K. (2006) *Partnering in design and construction*. New York: McGraw-Hill.

Goh, Y. M. (2021) *Introduction to workplace safety and health management* (2nd ed.). Singapore: World Scientific.

Greiman, V. (2013) *Megaproject management: Lessons on risk and project management from the Big Dig*. New York: Wiley.

Grondzik, W. (2009) *Principles of building commissioning*. New York: Wiley.

Imai, M. (2012) *Gemba kaizen*. New York: McGraw-Hill.

Kiran, D. (2016) *Total quality management*. London: Butterworth-Heinemann.

Moran, M. (2003) *Construction safety handbook*. Maryland: ABS Consulting.

Ohno, T. (1988) *Toyota production system*. New York: Productivity Press.

Plowman, C. and Diffendal, J. (2020) *Project communications*. New York: Business Expert Press.

Rubin, R., Fairweather, V., and Guy, S. (1999) *Construction claims*. New York: Van Nostrand Reinhold.

CHAPTER 12

Construction

Project monitoring and control

During the construction phase, the contractor implements the baseline plans and makes suitable adjustments. He also manages the resources, project progress, documentation, claims, and disputes. This chapter covers the possible key changes to the baseline plans. Some plans require only minor changes and, to avoid repetition, they will not be discussed here.

Scope changes

Scope changes are inevitable in large projects, and they must be within the original scope of the contract. For example, a change from a school to a prison is beyond the scope of a "school." Scope creep, or small changes in scope, can occur through marginal design changes.

Sponsors may require scope changes because of business considerations, such as to alter production capacity because of changing product demand or there is a change in building code or regulation. The contractor may also initiate scope changes if there are differing site conditions, defective specifications, or a specified product is not available. Scope changes are common in software development projects because there are many users or departments and each wants to tailor the software to their current business procedures.

A *differing site condition* is one that differs from the contract documents or which the contractor does not reasonably expect. Since it does not make sense for each bidder to conduct soil tests on the site prior to tender, the sponsor normally supplies the soil test data "for information only," implying that bidders should conduct their due diligence. However, given the lack of site access and the short time for tender, contractors price their bids based on the sponsor-supplied data. Hence, when site conditions differ from the soil test data, the contractor expects the sponsor or her representative to issue a *variation order* (VO) or change order to instruct the contractor to make changes. Generally, the sponsor takes this risk because, as explained earlier, it is not reasonable to expect the contractor to conduct detailed soil tests before tender. If the sponsor shifts the risk to the contractor, the latter will include a high contingency sum and stands to gain if the differing conditions do not occur. The tender may also attract a risky bidder that puts a low contingency sum.

However, if the site conditions are expected from the sponsor's soil test data and the contractor did not exercise due diligence at time of bid, the sponsor does not need to issue a VO. We assume that sponsors do not intentionally hide site information to avoid paying for extra work.

The VO process starts with either the sponsor's project team or the contractor. In the former case, the sponsor's side requires scope changes. In the latter case, the contractor discovers the need for VO. Both sides need to agree on the cost and schedule impact of the proposed VO. If they disagree, one option is for the initiator to withdraw the VO. The contractor may revise or pursue as submitted, escalating it to a *claim*, that is, an unsettled benefit a contractor believes he is entitled. Both sides should use a VO log to track changes (Table 12.1).

A VO is a formal written request. It is possible for a sponsor to informally request for scope changes. It is called a *constructive change* and, in the absence of a formal request, can lead to disputes.

Table 12.1   VO log.

		Outcome				
VO proposal	Description	Submit	Approved	Rejected	Revised	VO No.	Amount ($)

Schedule changes

Recall from Chapter 11 that the contractor has a project schedule. As shown in Table 12.2, activity (or work package) "A" did not start on time and will extend into week 4. The planned duration is "x" and the actual duration is marked as capital letter "X." Both the sponsor and contractor will note the reasons for the delay because they are likely to be forgotten when disputes arise months later.

The critical path is A-B-D-F, shown in boldface font in column 2 of Table 12.2. Since "A" is on the critical path, the contractor will need to make changes to the schedule to avoid delaying the project. For example, the sponsor may issue a VO to direct the contractor to accelerate the work.

The asterisk on activity D indicates a project milestone. A project has a few milestones that need careful tracking.

Cost changes

In Table 12.3, we show how the quantities and costs for *work package* "A," which has three components (A1, A2, and A3), are monitored. At this

Table 12.2   Monitoring of project schedule.

Task ID	Description	Duration	1	2	3	4	5	6	7	8	9	10	11	12	13	14
1	**A**	3	x	x	x											
				X	X	X										
2	**B**	4		x		x	x	x	x							
3	C	2				x	x	x	f							
4	**D***	5							x	x	x		x	x		x
5	E	1					x	x	f	f	f		f	f		f
6	**F**	2												x	x	x
	Equipment		2	2	3	3										
	Labor		5	5	6	6	5	5	4	4	4	4	3	3	3	3
	Materials						4	3	3	3	3	3	2	2		
	Subcon Y					x	x	x								
	Subcon Z						x	x								

Table 12.3   Variance report for Work Package "A."

Work Package: A										
Cost code:								Date:		
	Qty	Quantities				Costs ($)				
Item	(m²)	PW	TW	TD	%C	PW	TW	TD	EC	Budget
A1	100	30	20	50	50	30,000	5,000	35,000	70,000	65,000
A2	150	50	10	60	40	50,000	4,000	54,000	80,000	80,000
A3	200	60	50	110	55	60,000	9,000	69,000	90,000	85,000
									240,000	230,000

PW: Previous week   %C: Percentage completed
TW: This week   EC: Estimated cost
TD: To date

point, the contractor expects the work package, when completed, to exceed the budget by $10,000.

To monitor quantities and costs for the *entire project*, the contractor uses Table 12.4. The layout is similar to Table 12.3 except that each item refers to a work package (WP) rather than components of a work package.

At any period t before the completion of construction (T), there are three cost variables, namely, actual cost (AC), budget (B) or planned cost, and earned value (EV) (Figure 12.1). The actual cost and budget are obtained by summing up the cost of the work packages as shown in the last row of Table 12.4.

The cost variance (CV) is

$$CV = AC - EV$$

where EV is the value of work completed, that is,

$$EV = \text{Percentage of work completed} \times B$$

For example, if $B = \$10$ m and only 30% of the work is completed at time t, then $EV = \$3$ m.

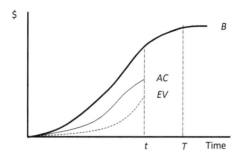

Figure 12.1   Project costs.

Table 12.4   Project variance report.

Project:									
Date:									
WP	Qty (m²)	Quantities				Costs ($)				
		PW	TW	TD	%C	PW	TW	TD	EC	Budget
A	450	140	80	220	49	140,000	18,000	158,000	240,000	230,000
B										
C										
D										
E										
F										
							AC		*B*

Quality

Recall from Chapter 11 that the contractor's quality plan comprises quality principles to improve the products, services, and processes. These principles are applied to inputs, inventory, storage, subcontractors, equipment, drawings, and documents to reduce defects.

Some countries have systems for evaluating the contractor's output quality, such as Singapore's Construction Quality Assessment System (CONQUAS), which was developed in 1989. It assesses the structural, architectural, mechanical, and electrical works in building projects.

Contractors with good CONQUAS scores will have a competitive advantage when tendering for projects.

Resource management

During execution, the contractor needs to manage resources comprising materials, labor, equipment, and subcontractors.

Materials need to be sourced, procured, transported, stored, and protected from spoilage and theft. Sponsors normally require the contractor to prepare a schedule of submittals that include shop drawings, product data, warranties, samples, test reports, and energy calculations. The contractor, subcontractors, fabricators, and manufacturers submit these items to the sponsor's project team for approval or review before using or installing them on site.

A typical process is for the subcontractor to submit shop drawings from a fabricator to the contractor. The contractor reviews the drawings, verifies the materials, measurements, and construction method, and stamps the drawing as "Reviewed" before passing them to the sponsor's project team. The sponsor's team may approve, ask for corrections, or reject the drawings. The team informs the contractor of the decision and the latter conveys it to the subcontractor.

Designers prefer to "review" rather than "approve" shop drawings to reduce liability. They approve the design *intent* rather than the details, and argue that the contractor is responsible for making all components fit together. A subcontractor or fabricator should take final field measurements before fabrication.

The submittal process can be cumbersome if designers reject shop drawings or require revisions. A more efficient way is for the parties to meet, reduce the information required, or submit similar items as a single package.

Many construction projects hire a mix of foreign workers, unionized workers, and non-unionized local labor. Contractors need to provide supervision, possibly housing, safe conditions, fair treatment, and incentives to improve productivity. In addition, productivity depends on the weather, regulatory quality, functioning of markets, input supply, efficiencies of processes, worker education, experience, and skills, working hours, and the technologies embodied in different types of equipment.

Generally, construction productivity is lower than that of other sectors such as manufacturing. Apart from the above factors, there is insufficient research and development (R&D) because of thin profit margins from competitive tenders. Further, the project team is temporarily assembled for the development and this makes it difficult to improve productivity from *learning by doing* (Tan and Elias, 2000). In other words, the team does not have a chance to improve its productivity by working together for longer periods. Finally, unlike manufacturing, there are few *scale economies* in construction because every project is unique.

We can measure productivity (A) as a residual using the index number approach, that is,

$$\log (A_t/A_{t-1}) = \log(Q_t/Q_{t-1}) - \alpha\log(K_t/K_{t-1}) - \beta\log(L_t/L_{t-1})$$

where Q is output, K is capital input, and L is labor input. The parameters α and β are factor shares for capital and labor respectively, t denotes time, and $\log(.)$ is the natural logarithm function. The Tornqvist index (Tornqvist, 1936) uses dynamic factors shares, that is, α is the average of capital factor shares between adjacent periods, and similarly for β. To determine factor shares, we require wages rates for different categories of workers and rental rates for different types of capital.

The main difficulty in measuring productivity lies in ascertaining the capital input because we need to aggregate different types of capital of differing vintages, such as computers, machines, equipment, vehicles, and buildings. There will also be difficulties in determining the rates of depreciation and extent of capacity utilization. Hence, it is more common to measure only labor productivity, which is simply Q/L. This ignores capital input and technical change. Even here, it is possible to mismeasure construction output Q and labor input L because of quality differences. If prices are used, such as if we use contract value as Q, price changes will affect the value of Q, which is undesirable. If we use physical units such as per unit of floor area constructed, there are many different types of buildings, making it difficult to compare productivity across firms and countries.

Lastly, the contractor needs to manage subcontractors. The contractor should be included as an additional insured party in the subcontractor's insurance policy as protection against third-party claims. Effective coordination of work with subcontractors requires close supervision, regular meetings, timely release of information ahead of schedule, addressing safety and health concerns, and proper documentation. Finally, subcontractors need to be paid promptly when they submit their payment requests to the contractor. The latter consolidates the requests and submits them to the sponsor for payment. The sponsor's project team, and possibly the lender's consultant, will then measure and certify actual progress. In the past, contractors pay subcontractors only when they are paid by sponsors or have the funds and are willing to do so. Some countries have introduced the Security of Payment Act to expedite payment (Lim, 2020).

Progress reports

The contractor's project team submits two reports. The project manager submits a weekly or monthly progress report to senior management on the following:

- scope changes and VOs;
- cost changes and analysis;
- schedule changes and analysis;
- subcontractors;
- suppliers; and
- issues.

In turn, the contractor submits a project progress report to the sponsor based on inputs from the project manager.

The superintendent submits a daily report (also called daily logs or diaries) to the project manager on

- weather;
- general field progress;
- presence of subcontractors and their workforce by craft and equipment;
- deliveries;

- occurrences and reasons;
- visitors; and
- issues.

These reports may include progress images. They may also be used for settling future disputes.

Managing documents

During construction, the contractor will manage documents associated with each baseline plan. These documents include

- communication records such as minutes of meetings and correspondences;
- safety records;
- visitor and official inspection logs;
- drawings;
- submittals records;
- contract documents;
- insurances and bonds;
- progress reports and images;
- labor records;
- materials purchase, payment, warranties, and other records;
- equipment purchase, maintenance, and other records;
- payment, cost, and budget reports;
- variation orders; and
- close-out records.

Many of these documents will be stored electronically in databases.

Claims and disputes

Recall that a claim is an unsettled benefit a contractor believes she is entitled. The causes of claims include (Netscher, 2016)

- differing site conditions;
- relocation of work by sponsor;

- lack of site access;
- design changes or insufficient detail;
- defective specifications;
- design errors and omissions;
- acceleration of work as directed by sponsor;
- unnecessary restrictions on methods;
- interrupted work;
- sponsor furnishes equipment or materials late or in poor condition;
- late inspections, reviews, or approvals;
- force majeure events;
- late payment;
- failure to agree on VO pricing;
- variations in quantities in unit price contracts;
- rejection of requested substitutions; and
- improper work rejection.

A claim may escalate into a *dispute*. While claims are in progress, the contractor cannot stop work. Obviously, the sponsor's project team may challenge a claim, which is why claims require evidence and proper documentation (Rubin *et al.*, 1999).

There are many ways to reduce claims, such as equitable risk allocation, better contract and other information, effective project management, partnering, and proper documentation (Levin, 2016).

Claims may be resolved through *negotiation*, failing which both parties may seek third-party *reconciliation*. If this does not solve the problem, the next stage is for both parties to appoint a *mediator*. Some projects use a dispute review board comprising three members to make the recommendations. Both parties appoint the board members prior to the start of construction.

If the desire is for binding decisions, rather than just recommendations, there are several options. *Adjudication* is a statutory process of hearing disputes, such as payment issues between the contractor and subcontractor. In *arbitration*, both parties appoint an arbitrator who then makes a binding decision. The most costly option is *litigation*, where parties settle it in court. It is the last resort. In a *default judgment*, the defendant fails to enter appearance or file her defense. A second type of decision is a *summary judgment* where the plaintiff can show that the defendant has no real defense. The defendant will try to show that this is not the case and claim for a full trial.

Apart from differing site conditions discussed early in the chapter, another common area of dispute is delays along the critical path and the project cannot be finished on time (Nagata *et al.*, 2017). If the contractor causes the non-excusable delay, the sponsor can impose liquidated damages. Similarly, if the sponsor causes the non-excusable delay, the contractor can expect extension of time and possible compensation. If both parties cause an overlapping or concurrent delay, the resolution depends on contract clauses. If the contract is silent on this matter, then there is usually no compensation but the contractor may be given extension of time. For example, if the sponsor is late in providing the drawings and this overlaps with the contractor's delay by his subcontractor, then the contractor may ask for extension of time.

Finally, there is the serious possibility of early termination of the construction contract because of the contractor's poor performance, the sponsor runs out of funds, there is a force majeure event, or there is frustration of contract. A frustration of contract occurs if either party is unable to perform because of unforeseen circumstances. For example, if the contractor does not have access to the site, he cannot perform and there is no breach of contract. The sponsor must seek the lender's approval to terminate the construction contract early, and the three parties will not take this lightly. The lender may exercise her step-in rights under the Direct Agreement as discussed in Chapter 7.

References

Levin, P. (Ed.) (2016) *Construction contract claims, changes, and dispute resolution*. Virginia: ASCE.

Lim, P. (2020) *Contract administration and procurement in the Singapore construction industry*. Singapore: World Scientific.

Nagata, M., Manginelli, W., Lowe, S., and Trauner, T. (2017) *Construction delays (3rd Edition): Understanding them clearly, analyzing them correctly*. London: Elsevier.

Netscher, P. (2016) *Construction claims: A short guide for contractors*. Perth: Panet Publications.

Rubin, R., Fairweather, V., and Guy, S. (1999) *Construction claims*. New York: Wiley.

Tan, W. and Elias, Y. (2000) Learning by doing in Singapore construction. *Journal of Construction Research*, 2, 151–58.

Tornqvist, L. (1936) The Bank of Finland's consumption price index. *Bank of Finland Monthly Bulletin*, 10, 1–8.

Chapter 13

Project close-out

Close-out activities

As the construction nears completion, the various parties need to manage and coordinate the following close-out activities (Mincks and Johnston, 2017):

- conduct start-up and testing;
- rectify punch lists, conduct inspections, and do final cleaning;
- apply for statutory approvals;
- certify completion of construction;
- hand over documents;
- prepare for operation and maintenance (O&M);
- release resources; and
- evaluate project and debrief participants.

We discuss these activities below.

Start-up and testing

The contractor will arrange for the commissioning, startup, and testing of the various systems. Depending on the system to the tested, the attendees may include the sponsor, the project team, contractor, commissioning experts, relevant authorities, subcontractors, suppliers, and manufacturers.

Punch lists, inspections, and cleaning

The contractor will compile and prepare several categorized punch lists from the sponsor's project team. A punch list consists of items that require rectification. The sponsor's project team will seek additional inputs from users when compiling the lists.

The contractor and subcontractors will then rectify the items for inspection by the owner's team. There will also be a final cleaning and inspection before the contractor hands over the facility to the sponsor.

Statutory approvals

Generally, the sponsor needs to apply for a *certificate of statutory completion* (CSC) from the relevant building authority. It certifies the completion of building works. In many cases, not all works are complete and the sponsor applies for a *temporary occupation permit* (TOP) first to allow tenants and users to occupy the building.

Completion of construction

When most of the project works are completed, the designers will issue a *certificate of substantial completion* to the contractor. In some countries, it is called the certificate of practical completion. The issuance starts the clock for the defects liability period (DLP), warranties, and liquidated damages for project delay, if any. The sponsor will also take over the responsibilities for property and liability insurance, routine maintenance, utilities, and security.

When the minor works are also completed, the designers will issue a *certificate of final completion*. The designers will process the final payment and settle all outstanding claims for the sponsor to make the final payment and release half the retainage. The other half will be released after the defects liability period, when all defects have been satisfactorily rectified. In some countries, the sponsor requires the contractor to obtain lien release or waivers from suppliers and subcontractors to ensure that they have been paid by the contractor.

If there are energy and other performance requirements or targets such as Leadership in Energy and Environmental Design (LEED), Green Building, Building Wellness, or carbon credit certification, the relevant authorities, designers or consultants will issue the certificates (Kibert, 2016).

Documentation

The contractor will need to archive the project records for his own use. In addition, he will need to hand over the following items to the sponsor:

- building user guide for the various building systems;
- testing and commission results;
- certificates and warranties;
- as-built drawings;
- copies of statutory permits, licenses, and approvals; and
- BIM files from the common data environment.

The contract may stipulate additional items to hand over, such as software to operate certain systems.

Preparation for operation and maintenance

To prepare for the operation and maintenance (O&M) phase, the contractor will hand over the building owner's operation and maintenance manual, spare parts, tools, extra materials, and O&M data to the sponsor. There will also be training sessions for operatives.

Release of resources

The contractor will begin to redeploy his resources to other projects as the construction nears completion. The project office will be progressively downsized until a small team remains during the defects liability period.

Evaluation and debrief

The project evaluation and debrief may take place in two sessions, one for direct project participants after final payment, and the other for users a few months after occupation (Preiser *et al.*, 2016). The purpose is to gather feedback from all parties on performance and areas for improvement. In particular, we should also assess the performance of key stakeholders on their collective responsibilities for the social, economic, and environmental outcomes of the project.

The parties will need to access, retain, protect, develop, and share the critical and often tacit or experiential knowledge gained from the project (O'dell and Hubert, 2011). The sharing may take the form of mentoring, networking among communities of practice, and transfer of best practices for future projects.

It is simplistic to expect genuine feedback if the parties fear repercussions for voicing criticisms. There needs to be a balance of positives and negatives, tact, and a real interest to improve. Otherwise, we end up with feedback that are not specific, minor, or of no consequence (Stone and Heen, 2015).

References

Kibert, C. (2016) *Sustainable construction: Green building design and delivery.* New York: Wiley.

Mincks, W. and Johnston, H. (2017) *Construction jobsite management.* Boston: Cengage Learning.

O'dell, C. and Hubert, C. (2011) *The new edge in knowledge: How knowledge management is changing the way we do business.* New York: Wiley.

Preiser, W., White, E., and Rabinowitz, H. (2016) *Post-occupancy evaluation.* London: Routledge.

Stone, D. and Heen, S. (2015) *Thanks for the feedback: The science and art of receiving feedback well.* New York: Penguin.

CHAPTER 14

Operation and maintenance

Goals of asset management

The operation and maintenance (O&M) phase is the longest period in a Public Private Partnership (PPP) contract, often lasting throughout the asset life, and typically more than 20 years. Normally, the SPV appoints an operator for the facility through an O&M contract as discussed in Chapter 7. The operator may be a shareholder or an external party. If it is the former, there are possible conflicts of interest and inefficiencies arising from lack of competitive tender.

There are two levels of asset management, namely, the portfolio level comprising a group of assets, and the individual asset level. In this chapter, we will deal with physical assets, rather than financial assets. At the portfolio level, the organization focus is on the composition of the assets that, in turn, affects the overall performance in terms of risks and returns. For example, if the special purpose vehicle (SPV) holds a group of road assets, it needs to decide which assets to buy or sell in the portfolio. At the individual asset level, the goal is to optimize the asset life-cycle performance. When combined with portfolio considerations, the sponsor needs to consider the asset's performance and ways to realize asset value through asset enhancement, securitization, or by selling it.

Operation and maintenance contract

The contract for the operation of an infrastructure asset is separate from that of building services. For a train system, the operation includes scheduling, ticketing, signaling, and so on. In contrast, a building services contract provides security, air-conditioning, cleaning, and so on. However, sponsors often combine these two functions as a single contract because of the close linkages.

The sponsors may appoint an experienced and creditworthy operator or choose to manage the facility themselves if a sponsor has experience in managing similar assets. However, sponsors will have to manage the possible conflicts of interest. Another option is to appoint the contractor as the operator for the first few years, if the contractor has the relevant operating experience.

The O&M contract is a short-term fixed-price contract or, more likely, a cost-plus-fee agreement with penalties for poor performance. The latter arrangement avoids the operator's uncertainties with costs and hence the need for the SPV to pay a risk premium. With short contracts, the SPV can then flexibly change the operator, contract terms and conditions, and price after every few years. The SPV may impose a maximum price on the cost-plus-fee arrangement and a bonus scheme to incentivize the operator to control costs.

If the SPV experiences a shortfall in funds from revenue or cost changes during this phase, it will require equity injections from existing or new shareholders through subordinated debt. The project lender may lend to the SPV to cover temporary shortfalls or require the establishment of an O&M contingency fund.

Operation and maintenance program

An O&M program integrates the operation, maintenance, engineering support, training, and administration (OMETA) of the facility to improve process efficiency, reliability, and safety. The application of OMETA to infrastructure assets depends on the type, complexity, and size of assets (Meador, 1995).

Integration requires the coordination of the various elements of OMETA. For example, the operation may require engineering support to modify the design for upgrading existing assets or build new works. Engineering support is also required for the training of operatives, repairs, and maintenance. We discuss the elements of OMETA below.

Operation

The operation of a facility requires a governance structure that identifies roles and responsibilities, decision-making, and monitoring of progress.

For a small facility, the O&M manager reports to the Director of Administration of the SPV. An assistant manager or executive assists him, and most services are subcontracted out. For large facilities, the Director of Facilities manages different managers for projects, planning and design, and O&M. In addition, there may be a facility manager at each site reporting to the O&M manager.

The effective implementation and control of operations require smooth coordination with the other elements of OMETA. The operator needs to

- use approved procedures;
- closely monitor operating conditions and parameters to optimize asset performance;
- secure materials, fuel, labor, and utilities inputs;
- perform appropriate diagnostics and testing;
- conduct emergency planning and responses; and
- ensure proper documentation.

It is the operator's responsibility to keep proper reports, records, and operating logs. If there are operational delays caused by force majeure events or the SPV, the operator is normally entitled to an equitable adjustment.

Maintenance

The operator develops a maintenance program that comprises a mixture of corrective, preventive, and predictive maintenance. The performance of a maintenance program may be measured in terms of operational efficiency, reliability, and safety.

A maintenance program is necessary because ad hoc corrective maintenance, done only when assets malfunction, is likely to result in higher life-cycle cost. Putting maintenance "last" in the list of priorities because it is a cost center will result in higher capital and running costs and reduced reliability. The life-cycle cost of an asset (L) is given by (Dell'Isola and Kirk, 2003)

$$L = -C + \Sigma \{M_t/(1 + k)^t\} + R/(1 + k)^T,$$

where C is the initial capital cost, M_t is the operation, maintenance, and repair costs at time t, R is the residual value at the end of the asset life (T), and k is the discount rate. The summation goes from $t = 1$ to $T - 1$. An asset may have a high investment cost but low operation, maintenance, and repair costs, and vice versa. Hence, a "run until it fails" reactive maintenance philosophy is unlikely to achieve minimum life-cycle cost. Note that life-cycle comparisons among assets are inappropriate if the assets have different T values and if the benefits from operating the assets differ.

Recall from the previous chapter that the contractor should hand over O&M manuals for the various equipment and systems during the close-out stage. Without the required technical information, it is difficult to carry out proper maintenance work.

Preventive or routine maintenance is carried out periodically using time or physical measures, such as weekly or after every x km for vehicles. From an inventory list of equipment for the facility, the operator categorizes and prioritizes the critical ones. Over longer periods, the operator conducts cyclical maintenance or replacement of major assets such as elevators and pumps.

Unlike time-based or physical-based preventive maintenance, predictive maintenance is carried out based on the actual condition of the asset. This requires forecasting the actual asset stress, which may require costly diagnostic equipment and training. In reliability-centered maintenance, which is adopted by airlines and sectors that require high reliability, we identify key components that may fail and then devise the corrective maintenance tasks (Bloom, 2005).

Engineering support

O&M activities require engineering support for system changes such as modification, refurbishment, building new equipment, and configuration management in response to new requirements. These new requirements may arise because of new regulations, changing priorities, or the current performance is not achieving the target. Designing the new configuration requires engineering studies of data and impact, recommendations, configuration control, and documentation (Watts, 2015; Lian, 2019).

Training

The effective implementation of O&M activities requires control of training programs to ensure the skills gaps are plugged and training is relevant. A common training gap is the effective use of computerized systems to administer O&M functions. There should also be training on emergency response.

Administration

The administration of O&M activities covers policies for planning, assessment, and control involving budgeting and finance, cost tracking, human resources, processes, security, space management, user services, technical services, configuration control, utility usage, inventory, documentation, regulatory compliance as well as safety, health, and environmental requirements. There are many computerized maintenance management software (CMMS) that support and integrate these administrative functions.

Insurance

During the O&M phase, insurance coverage is similar, that is, the operator needs to purchase insurance to cover worker injury, employer's liability, general liability, and property. The SPV is included as additional insured under general liability. The operator furnishes the SPV with copies of certificates of insurance.

Asset enhancement

Asset enhancement initiatives (AEI) refer to asset upgrades that increase net lettable area (NLA), lower costs, or improve asset value. An increase in NLA raises revenue. It is also possible to lower operating costs, such as by installing energy-efficient devices or solar panels. Finally, many upgrades improve asset value, such as by refurbishing restrooms, escalators, dining areas, and lifts.

Realizing asset value

Sponsors need not wait until the end of the PPP contract to realize asset value. A sponsor may sell her shares to existing shareholders or an external party depending on the terms of the shareholders' agreement. Often, this requires the approval of the lender and grantor to ensure that the SPV will continue to function effectively.

Alternatively, the sponsors may decide to sell the SPV collectively to a third party, which may be an infrastructure fund with expertise in running the project. Sponsors have different reasons for selling out, such as profitability, change in priority, perceived new risks, cash flow considerations, or difficulties working together. The infrastructure fund may securitize the asset by issuing new shares to other investors. In this way, it can raise funds by pooling infrastructure assets and issuing stapled securities. The pool is often well-diversified to reduce risks and achieve stable returns.

References

Bloom, N. (2005) *Reliability-centered maintenance*. New York: McGraw-Hill.

Dell'Isola, A. and Kirk, S. (2003) *Life-cycle costing for facilities*. Massachusetts: Reed Construction Data.

Lian, J. (2019) *Facilities planning and design*. Singapore: World Scientific.

Meador, R. (1995) *Maintaining the solution to operations and maintenance efficiency improvement*. World Energy Engineering Congress, Atlanta, Georgia.

Watts, F. (2015) *Configuration management for senior managers*. London: Butterworth-Heinemann.

CHAPTER 15

Handing over

Early termination

Either party may voluntarily terminate the project early. However, if the special purpose vehicle (SPV) terminates the project early, such as, if it is insolvent or breaches the contract, it is likely to incur a loss. A grantor may also terminate the project early because of policy changes and compensate the SPV.

If the SPV terminates the project during construction, the grantor will have to find another party to take over, which is costly and messy. If the termination occurs during the Operation and Maintenance (O&M) phase, compensation is likely. A basis for compensation, is the present value of future net cash flows the SPV loses upon early termination.

Project participants do not take voluntary termination lightly. If the SPV is facing financial difficulties, there may be other options apart from voluntary termination. These options include equity injections by existing or new investors, restructuring of loans, or renegotiation of the Public Private Partnership (PPP) contract. The latter include lengthening the concession period, tariff adjustment or changes in performance criteria.

Handing over issues

Preparation for handing over of the asset begins about three years before the end of the contract. Depending on the PPP contract terms, the issues concern the quality of the asset and possible compensation if the asset is of poor quality.

The grantor will carry out an early inspection and quality audit to determine which assets require improvement prior to handing over.

The grantor may carry out the audit or both parties appoint an independent assessor.

If the quality of the assets is unsatisfactory, the SPV will have to make good or compensate the grantor.

Finally, the operator will also need to hand over the documents including operating manuals, reports, drawings, records, and logs. Importantly, the operator has a long time series of operating data that are useful for predicting asset performance and energy consumption using evidence-based maintenance and data analytics (Campbell and Reyes-Picknell, 2015). Hence, the quality and types of data to hand over should be part of contract requirement.

By studying the performance, the grantor may appoint the same operator during the initial years to smoothen the transition, which includes training of new operatives. Other items to hand over include spare parts and excess materials.

Reference

Campbell, J. and Reyes-Picknell, J. (2015) *Uptime: Strategies for excellence in maintenance management.* London: CRC Press.

Lightning Source UK Ltd.
Milton Keynes UK
UKHW021835270421
382734UK00004B/221